Care and Counselling Series

YOU ALONE CARE

BOOKS ON CARE AND COUNSELLING

Library of Pastoral Care

Pastoral Care in Hospitals
NORMAN AUTTON

The Pastor and His Ministry
OWEN BRANDON

In His Own Parish:
Pastoral Care through Parochial Visiting
KENNETH CHILD

Working with Children
ANTHONY DENNEY

Understanding the Adolescent
MICHAEL HARE DUKE

Casework and Pastoral Care
JEAN HEYWOOD

Marriage Counselling
KENNETH PRESTON

Care and Counselling Series

Peace at the Last
NORMAL AUTTON

Principles of Pastoral Counselling
R. S. LEE

Sexual Counselling
UNA KROLL

Heather McKenzie

YOU ALONE CARE

LONDON
SPCK

First published 1980
SPCK
Holy Trinity Church
Marylebone Road
London NW1 4DU

Set, printed and bound in Great Britain by
Fakenham Press Limited, Fakenham, Norfolk

ISBN 0 281 03758 2

I loved her most, and thought to set my rest on
her kind nursery... *King Lear* (Act I: Scene I)

ACKNOWLEDGEMENT

I wish to thank: Mr Paul Richard, solicitor; Mrs Elaine Steele, hospital matron; Miss Doris Belcher, barrister.

My views are not necessarily the views of the National Council for the Single Woman and her Dependants.

H.M.

Contents

ONE
The Objectives of this Book

The prime objectives of this book are to help to alleviate the burdens of single persons who care for elderly disabled, or infirm parents, or other relatives, and so in turn to help to make their dependants' last years happy and serene.

Ageing, though natural, is not an easy process for any of us. This is true, particularly in the case of those who are infirm or disabled. For them the present and the future can be especially bleak, full of apprehension, and foreboding.

We all gain a sense of security from things with which we are familiar. A home, a neighbourhood with its well-known inhabitants, with their well-known idiosyncrasies, are sources of comfort and sometimes of amusement, providing a sense of permanence in what we from time to time realize is an impermanent world. Such feelings are especially reinforced by the presence of family around us. This can, where there is mutual love and understanding, generate the peace and warmth of a continuing sense of belonging and of feeling wanted. In circumstances where such emotional ties exist, there can be no gainsaying the advantage to the dependant from familial care in her own environment.

For the carer, filial love can be a dominant emotion. Many, but by no means all adult children, with strong parental ties, can find profound self-satisfaction and fulfilment in caring for those whom they love and who have grown so infirm that they can no longer cope alone.

Happily, many carers enjoy their years of caring and it is reassuring to know that the majority say that they would happily do it again. But this is not true of all carers, and some may possibly find themselves under severe mental and physical strain. Such people may need help and support.

In this book I have identified typical caring situations; discussed basic home-nursing procedures; briefly touched

1

on the most common health problems of the elderly; looked at the areas of potential emotional strain; provided you with information on people and services which can be of help; explained what to do when someone dies; discussed pertinent financial benefits and finance generally; advised on how to save on heat and home maintenance and, for easy referral, appended the details of financial benefits and a list of helpful addresses.

Being specific, you should ask yourself:

Would you be realistic and accept that it is virtually impossible to pre-determine for how long you could be caring?

Would you know which supportive services to look for?

Would you know to which financial benefits she and you would be entitled, and under what conditions?

Could you look at the effect on your life short term and long term (such as how your career prospects would be affected and what they would be in perhaps 15 years' time!)?

Are you a strong enough personality not to let your identity merge with that of your parent; by implementing measures to ensure that as far as possible each of you will retain a sense of individuality and dignity.

Do you have a strong religious belief or philosophy of life that may help you?

Some carers gradually assume the role, almost without recognizing what is happening; others are confronted by a crisis—an old parent suddenly being unable to continue to cope because of severe illness or injury.

In an effort to avoid clumsy construction, I have referred, because this is typically the case, to the carer as 'she' and to 'mother' as the dependant. However nine-tenths of the information is applicable equally to the single man who cares, and to the father as a dependant.

I hope that what I have written will be helpful.

TWO

Caring Situations

When the time comes that your elderly parent can no longer manage adequately, there should be several courses of action open to you. The action you adopt will be determined by several factors, among which will be your love for and relationship with your parent, your sense of responsibility towards her, her physical proximity to you, your financial resources and hers, your parent's real state of infirmity or disability—and that means being sure she is receiving the appropriate medical treatment—the availability and diversity of supportive services and her and your attitude towards those services.

Additionally, family or social pressure can cause you to make a decision about your parent's care which is not always the right one, either for your parent, or for you, the prospective carer. The very idea of what other members of the family, or friends and neighbours will say, if your parent is found either very ill or worse, can have an overwhelming effect on your decision-making. There are complex emotional interactions in every caring situation.

On the basis of the above, you may be confronted with making any one of the following decisions: whether to leave your parent where she is until she really cannot cope; whether to leave your job and stay at home, assuming a full-time caring role; whether to continue to work and to care for her simultaneously; whether to take her to live with you; whether to leave your job and to go home to care for her; whether her infirmity is going to be your excuse for getting off the work treadmill, or whether to agree to her being admitted to nursing or residential care.

In the following pages I have outlined typical caring situations to help you to identify your own position. However, I

3

advise you to read the entire book so that you will be better able to put your overall problems into focus.

Leaving your mother to cope

One typical situation in which you may have to make the decision of whether or not to leave your mother to cope on her own, is at the time your father dies. Grief can mar your judgement about leaving her in the family house to look after herself, with the overall financial and maintenance responsibilities. She will very likely be particularly vulnerable at this time, and may not take too much persuading to give up her home, and to go and live with you. Your anxiety about her will of course be heightened if she is at all infirm or disabled.

It is her prerogative to carry on for as long as she wishes, and you should not interfere unless you have good grounds to believe she won't manage; such as where her behaviour is potentially a cause of danger to herself, another, or another's property. Perhaps if left to cope, she may not clean the upstairs rooms regularly, she may not cook the same variety of meals as before, she may leave your father's place set at table—but if she can get along fairly well, you should let her get on with her own life.

Pressure from family and friends can result in an old person's being uprooted before it is absolutely necessary. Your Auntie Jenny, or Mrs Bloggs from next door, may take you to one side and tell you that you really must take your mother to live with you, but neither Auntie Jenny nor Mrs Bloggs will be involved in compensating for having usurped your mother's independence.

In the event of your mother's being uncertain about trying to cope, if she will be accessible, reassure her that you will be there in the background, and that she only has to call you if she needs you. Try to elicit any identifiable fears she has, and, where possible, take constructive steps to allay them.

Among the aspects of solitary living which could cause her

concern are: anxiety about burglars, fear of falling and lying hurt for hours, fire starting, how she will cope with house and garden maintenance, shopping in winter, paying the bills out of her pension, or what will happen when her health does fail.

At security level, you can attach safety chains to the doors, give a neighbour duplicate keys to her front door, and if she or you can afford it, have a burglar alarm put in.

There are several steps you can take to ensure that she will not feel isolated, or in danger of being at risk if she falls or becomes ill. Have a telephone installed for her. Many people use the phone in the following way: they dial the number of a relative or friend at a fixed time each day, and let it ring twice as a signal that they are all right. If your mother uses this method of indicating that she is well, it won't cost her any-thing and you'll both be happier. Other old people put a disc in the window if they need help. Another arrangement is to ask the neighbours to go in sometime during the day, or at least to watch for signs of activity. The milkman and the postman are first-class vigilantes and they will generally be only too happy to raise any alarm. You can visit periodically and stock her food cupboard and re-order fuel.

You can have the gas cooker checked by British Gas, who will not charge her, have the electric wiring checked by the Electricity Board, who will do a free visual check on the housing wiring, and put in a fire extinguisher. If she lives in a house, you can buy her a dog, both as company, and as a guardian. A few simple installations will reduce the risk of accidents: having a light over the stairs, removing torn lino, and putting in a bar beside the bath.

As the worry of how to make financial ends meet can press heavily on many old people, you can sit down and work out a simple budget with her. If she owns her house, it may be possible for her to take out an annuity which will make more money available. You can see that the house is properly insulated (*see* Chapter Seven) to save on her heating bills. And you can check whether she is entitled to rent and rate rebates or a heating allowance.

If she is somewhat infirm or disabled, arrange for a home help to come who will break her isolation and take the burden of general housework off her. If a home help is not available, and if either of you can afford it, pay a cleaner to come in at least twice a week. Remember the social contact is probably more important than a clean house.

It is important, of course, to realize that leaving her to cope can put a heavy responsibility on you. Undoubtedly you will invest a lot of time and energy in visiting, helping and arranging some areas of her life. You will have to guard against her becoming demanding of both your time and energy, otherwise the strain of part-time caring will wear you down and tell on your health. Many people leave their jobs because they simply cannot cope with coming and going, assuming a large part of the general running of a parent's home and working full time.

Just because you are unmarried or widowed do not accept the overall responsibility if you have brothers or sisters. Let them accept their share of the responsibility. Unless you broach their involvement with them, they will generally be quite happy to let you have the full burden of caring.

If your parent is disabled and lives in a large house, suggest that she close the upstairs and convert the downstairs into full living quarters. If she pleads she can't afford to put in a bathroom downstairs, look into the possibility of any appropriate adaptations (on the recommendation of the domiciliary occupational therapist) being financed by the social services department. Otherwise, encourage her to take out a maturity loan to finance the alterations. (For these cases see Chapter Six.)

If a good relationship is to be maintained between you, it is imperative for her not to feel a burden. Continuing to foster a give-and-take attitude is important—ask her to hem your skirt or sew a curtain for you, while you vacuum under her bed and dust the picture rails. Remember that you should try to keep a role as a buffer and not as the mainstay of her needs. You will have a better chance of achieving this end if you don't unnecessarily undermine her independence and you don't commit yourself to any rigid pattern of support.

Keep in mind that specialized sheltered housing may be an alternative at the time when she can no longer cope in her own environment with the aid of the available statutory and voluntary supportive services and your back-up help (*see* p. 109).

Staying at home

If you have always lived at home and your mother becomes very infirm or disabled, you may feel that you have no option but to give up your work and care for her full time. Ask yourself whether you are sure that your parent is getting the appropriate treatment. Is she getting as much help as is acceptable, and could the house be adapted to better meet her needs?

You should be guided in coming to your decision by the advice of a professional who should be better placed to be objective. It is quite possible that she may direct you towards an adequate support team, for instance, a home help, a district nurse, meals on wheels, getting the neighbours to keep a watchful eye, bringing in a volunteer, and your mother going to a Day Centre or lunch club.

If there seems to be no alternative to your staying at home, you should be aware of the measures you can take to ensure that you do not become fully immersed in caring, to the neglect of your own physical and mental health.

As a first step examine your financial situation. On the basis of your having been financially independent, you could find it very difficult to adapt to living on a reduced income. It is very important for you to realize that the Government does not in fact pay you to stay at home to care for a disabled parent. The real situation is that if your parent is in receipt of the Attendance Allowance, you will qualify for the Invalid Care Allowance (which carries with it Class I pension entitlements) (*see* Chapter Six). However, the qualifying

7

requirements for the Attendance Allowance are very stringent. Or if you can provide a medical certificate from your parent's GP which states that she cannot be left alone, you may qualify for supplementary benefit.

To avoid spending your money unnecessarily (as often happens), it is equally important for you to check whether or not the aids and equipment your parent needs are available from the local authority or the Red Cross. The district nurse will be able to advise you from where to borrow which equipment.

At a domestic level, it is essential for you to discuss the overall topic of finance with your mother, including the question of whether she is claiming all the allowances for which she may qualify, and come to some equitable arrangement through which each of you will fairly contribute to the outgoings. The need for a definite agreement about contributions cannot be stressed too much, as otherwise she may bank her pension and let you meet all the running expenses out of your resources. For instance, it is reasonable that if home maintenance or furniture is necessary, where feasible, your parent should meet the expense out of her resources (check whether she can get a Repairs Grant). If you do meet such expenses, keep all receipts. They may be valuable later.

As for protecting your own future, you should feel quite entitled to ask your mother to make provision for you under the terms of her will. Of course, you must be realistic, and if you have only been away from work for a short time, and have always lived at home, you would not be justified in asking her to make provision for you to the exclusion of your brothers and sisters, as they could rightly argue that, anyway, you had always had a free roof over your head. As to the appropriate clauses to be inserted in her will where provision would be justified see Chapter Nine.

The risk of social isolation is probably one of the most potentially destructive situations any single carer can have to face, and it can generally be obviated in a practical way. You

8

must remember that there are two entities in every caring situation: the dependent person—your mother—and the one taking care—you. Although undoubtedly you will see your main obligation as making her as comfortable as possible, it is very important for you, in achieving this end, not to lose your own sense of identity. This means that you must try to have a flexible caring pattern; you must accept offers by other members of the family to take part of the responsibility and you must try to bring in relief sitters-in; you must try to keep up contacts and interests; you must go on holiday and you must bring in appropriate supportive services. The tedium involved in making such arrangements will be well worth it. So many carers say 'Mother doesn't like strangers,' but the alternative often results in her daughter (or son) having a physical or mental breakdown and the mother's future then being put in question. Many elderly people exalt their own needs as their first priority, and become demanding and selfish or just generally make the carer's life a 'war of nerves'. If you find yourself being borne down, you will have to assert yourself. It won't be easy; in fact, it could prove to be very difficult. Reversal of roles can cause inner conflict or anguish, but don't become a 'slave' to your caring situation and don't drain away her self-dignity; in short, be attentive, but necessarily self-concerned. Equally, as far as possible, you must encourage her to keep up her contacts and interests.

To insulate yourself against the wear and tear of caring, if you can possibly manage it, take a holiday every year. If you can't find a substitute carer (the National Council for the Single Woman and Her Dependants (N.C.S.W.D.) has a list of such people) or if you can't afford for your mother to go into a short-stay nursing home (N.C.S.W.D. has a list) then ask your GP to admit her to a geriatric unit for two weeks. If you really can't bring yourself to go alone on holiday, or you really want to take her with you, locate a hotel which will cater to her needs (send for N.C.S.W.D.'s holiday circular for suitable addresses).

At the stage when your mother needs continuing care and your sleep is broken, ask her GP to implement what is called 'intermittent admission', so that you can get some rest.

You should read Chapter Four to get some idea of just what some of the caring challenges can be and how you may be able to cope with them.

If you begin to feel overwhelmed by her need for constant care, and you realize, or your doctor warns you, that your health is being affected, you may have to arrange either for her to go into hospital or into care (*see* Chapter Eight).

When you are still at work

Although you should stay at work for as long as you can, and only in otherwise insoluble situations give up your job, caring while simultaneously continuing to work, can be an exhausting mental and physical undertaking, which can seriously affect your health. While you are at work, the constant worry about how your disabled parent is coping, for instance if she is senile, whether she is hurting herself or has wandered off, can have an overwhelming effect on your ability to apply yourself to your job. The burden is augmented because when you leave work and go home in the evenings, you will have to assume actively the caring role with all its obligations and responsibilities.

The particular advantages of continuing to work can be seen in terms of financial security, the impossibility of becoming completely socially isolated, and in enabling you to retain your identity more easily.

Financially, (assuming your parent doesn't have the money) you should be able to afford some help in the house, and pay for relief sitters-in, to stay with your mother both while you are away during the day, and/or if you want to go out during the evening or weekend.

Continuing to work will give you a 'legitimate excuse' to get away from the caring scene, and preclude an intense caring dependency from building up. Protecting yourself against social isolation is vital to the retention of your mental and physical well-being, and staying at work is an assured method of achieving this. Single people who completely give up their interests and outside relationships, through giving priority to their parents' needs for companionship, can end up frustrated, angry, or repressed. What has to be borne in mind is that caring cannot be a pre-calculated involvement—it may go on for a few weeks or for thirty years, and any carer can slide into a pattern of social self-neglect. Therefore, if you are to have a well-balanced life, from the very outset, it is absolutely imperative to tell yourself that you are not to feel guilty if you go out. Where at all possible you must go out regularly. It is important to be able to recognize when your parent is being unreasonable. For instance, voiced groundless objections, or 'going silent' are not reasonable behaviour. Often carers are tired after a full day's work in addition to the housework and caring chores, and they feel they just can't cope with an outburst, so they avoid a scene at all cost. However, long term, it is in their interests to assert themselves. When you do go out, don't state any definite time at which you expect to return as your parent will worry inordinately if you aren't back precisely then. Be just a bit vague. Many of you will say, 'But she doesn't understand'; perhaps not, but what I do know are the unfortunate case histories of those who have not insisted on having some time to themselves.

Veteran carers probably will not be able to take the difficult step of getting some relief as their caring pattern will be too rigid; however, for those starting out, explain to your parent that you will be happy to keep her at home, but that you must dovetail caring for her with as normal a life for yourself as possible. A parent who really cares for a child will not want to see that child's health broken. If your parent is senile, try to judge what her reactions would have been before she became mentally ill.

You can relieve your parent's day-long isolation by providing help in the house (a home help if possible), arranging for meals on wheels, arranging for her friends or the neighbours to call, or by arranging for her to go to a Day Centre. The Attendance Allowance can be used to pay for sitters-in. Money, from whatever source, is well spent on sitter-in payments. If she is disabled, she may be encouraged to do more for herself if the house is better adapted to meet her needs. Ask the occupational therapist to advise you on this point. At an immediate practical level, you can leave her hobbies, the TV, radio and telephone accessible to her, and get her books from the library; perhaps a cat, dog or budgie could be acquired (cats' and dogs' toilet needs can be met by having a swing-door built into the back door).

It is equally important not to be a 'dogsbody' the moment you step over the threshold. A flexible schedule will prevent you from becoming overwhelmed by chores. Try to unwind for half an hour before you become involved in your caring role.

Perhaps your parent is the only person on whom you can bestow affection, but don't make a demanding spoilt 'child' of her; if you treat her with affection and respect and let her retain her dignity, you will have a much better chance of developing an acceptable carer-dependant relationship. It is essential to invoke all the statutory and voluntary supportive services that are available.

If your sleep is being continuously disturbed, in the first instance, ask the doctor to prescribe a tranquillizer for your mother; alternatively, ask him to arrange for her to be admitted at regular intervals to a geriatric unit. When you feel you can no longer cope with work and care, you may decide to give up your job (see below) or to allow her to be admitted to residential care (*see* Chapter Eight).

One advancement in the overall caring scene about which you should know is that special warden-serviced housing is being built for working women with elderly dependants, to ensure that the women can continue to work for longer.

The National Council for the Single Woman and Her Dependants will be happy to supply more details.

Taking your mother to live with you

The decision to take your mother to live with you should be taken only after you have thoroughly thought through the changes this could make in your lives. It is not a decision which should be made on the spur of the moment under pressure of an apparently immediate need.

Let us suppose that you are engrossed in your work, and a social worker telephones and tells you that your mother has had a stroke, is in hospital and the doctor reckons that she should be leaving hospital in a week's time. She goes on to tell you that, in the doctor's opinion, she should not be left to manage on her own at home. Then there is a silence at the other end of the phone and you realize that she is waiting for you to make a decision. Despite the urgency of her tone and the overwhelming sense of devotion or familial duty you may feel, don't make an 'on-the-spot' decision. Calmly and firmly tell her you will ring her back.

At this point, you may feel quite numb, bewildered and inclined to panic; but don't rush into a decision. Go and talk to someone who can be objective; your company welfare officer, your GP, or a long-standing friend.

Before coming to any decision, it is necessary to remind yourself that in taking your mother out of her own environment into yours, for whatever reason, a major adjustment on the part of each of you will be necessary. You must ask yourself whether, despite the apparent urgency of the impending situation, you would be equipped to cope with the implications of what may develop into a permanent arrangement. Would your mother adjust to being dependent on you; to shedding control over her own life and to some degree feeling herself to be a burden on you?

If you did uproot her, ask yourself how much you could compensate for the fundamental differences in her situation; for her not being mistress of the household (a role which she has perhaps had for fifty or sixty years), for not being in her familiar neighbourhood, for not having her friends around her, for having to change her GP and vicar.

For your part, you would have to give up part of the independence you have acquired. It is essential for you not to isolate yourself socially because your mother is with you. Would it be possible for each of you to escape to your own retreat if you wanted to? Would she be able to bring some of her own possessions so she could have tangible memories around her? And do you know which supportive services would be available for someone in her particular condition?

The next question you should ask yourself is what would be your course of action if her condition deteriorated to the point where she needed constant care? Would you be prepared to give up your work?

If, after considering both short- and long-term implications, you cannot see your way to a mutually happy arrangement, then surely it is more realistic to be honest, and to tell the social worker that you will take some leave and arrange for a private nurse to come in, or for her to go to a nursing home if she has a short-term disability, or if long-term, that you will arrange for her to be admitted to nursing and then geriatric care. Of course telling your mother will be difficult, but if you have a good relationship with her, she should understand.

On the other hand, if you decide to take her to live with you from the start, it is critical to the happiness of each of you that you do establish a living pattern that will provide each of you with privacy if you want it.

For your part, as far as possible, you should try to keep up your own routine and your comings and goings, your interests, and your friends; for her part, you must encourage her, as far as possible, to live her own life; encourage her to go out as much as possible, to develop new interests, and to take some part in running the household. In other words, foster her independence. Help her not to withdraw. Her degree of disability of course will influence just how self-sufficient she can be. As an example, if she has had a stroke, encourage her to persevere with physio-therapy, obtain what equipment you can to help her dress, etc.; ask her friends to visit, or

14

arrange for volunteers to come in to break her loneliness while you are at work. Try to ensure she has some entertainment—TV, radio, a good book, a hobby, etc., while you are away. Many elderly people enjoy having their own cassettes so that they can be in control of their own entertainment.

The question of finance should be resolved as soon as is decently possible. She will feel much better if she contributes towards the overall outgoings, and you will have fewer reservations about her living with you, if some financial formula, based on joint contribution, is worked out.

Although other members of the family may not pull their weight, don't discourage them from coming to see her or from her visiting them. Her whole family is important to her, and despite your unselfishness it is important for you to face the fact that you probably do not feature in her affections any more highly than they do.

Giving up your job and going home

You may decide that the only way you can be sure that your very infirm or disabled parent receives adequate care is for you to give up your job and go home.

Short term, the decision to go home would relieve your own anxiety, but you must look beyond that. Long term, your occupational pension would be affected, you would be in jeopardy of using up your savings, your chances of returning to subsequent employment would be reduced, and your physical and emotional health would be at risk through the combination of the constant strain of caring and the effects of increasing social isolation.

Undoubtedly, the advantages to your mother would be that her need for care would be met, and in the process, she would not have to be removed from her own environment, which should encourage a greater degree of self-sufficiency on her part for a longer period.

Now let us examine the ramifications on both your

15

mother's and your life, if you do actually give up your job and go home.

Financially, you must appreciate that you cannot qualify for the non-means-tested Invalid Care Allowance unless your mother receives the Attendance Allowance, and she can receive this only if her condition has so qualified her for six months preceding her claim (*see* Chapter Six). You are not entitled to supplementary benefit if you have capital of more than £1249, so you could readily find yourself having to use up your savings. Where possible, gear your actions to your mothers' condition. For instance, you should take leave of absence if the doctor's prognosis is that your mother's disease or illness is terminal.

Where your mother is rational, you must come to some financial arrangement based on a joint-contribution scheme. Check that she does not qualify for a rent and rate rebate. Many carers assume home maintenance expenses, replace furnishings, buy equipment, etc. and generally erode their savings, and their disabled parent saves her money for the family!

If at all possible, keep your own accommodation at least until it is obvious that you will not resume occupation within the foreseeable future. In this way you will be protecting your own roof, and because of its apparent proximity to your job (from which you have taken the precaution of taking only leave of absence) you will be protecting your own identity.

On the basis that short-term (despite any prognosis) can indeed become long-term, you must take positive steps towards preserving your own identity from the beginning of your caring involvement. Many carers make the mistake of setting a caring pattern on the basis that the caring is short term, and the result is that any subsequent desired change becomes almost impossible to implement.

The constructive steps you can take to protect your own identity are to be flexible in your schedule both in giving some time to yourself, and in ensuring that you do not permit an intense interdependency pattern to build up. A sick person often needs a psychological 'prop', your mother may tend to develop unreasonable possessive characteristics, and you may find it difficult to assert your independence. You must introduce whatever relief services are applicable. Ask your GP to arrange for the district nurse to bath her and if your local authority home help organizer is agreeable, get in a home help (most local authorities are far sighted about the need for you to get some relief, particularly where your mother is badly disabled and requires a lot of care). Contact volunteer groups in your area and arrange for sitters-in to come in. Although you may have a splendid relationship with your parent, and although you may feel quite able to get on with coping, you do need some respite. I cannot emphasize this need too much. Leaving your job, your own place, your colleagues, and the living pattern you have established over the years, will have an impact on you, and despite your efforts to accept the changes, you will almost certainly gradually begin to miss your old 'set-up'. Furthermore, it is wise to let your mother accept others such as the district nurse and home help on the scene before they actually become an essential part of it. Additionally, it is fair for her not to be isolated only with your constant company. Discourage her from developing the attitude that she wants only you there. If you give in to this form of possessiveness you will progressively shut out the idea of volunteers and the primary health-care team support, and struggle on to the ultimate severe detriment to your own health. (*See* Chapter Five where the social services are further discussed.)

Another method of lessening the caring burden is to implement available aids and equipment. Ask the district nurse or the social worker about aids and adaptations and equipment appropriate to your mother's case. Perhaps your job will be made easier if the house is adapted to accommodate your mother's disablement—ramps, handrails, etc, can help her to be more mobile. Always consider whether the bedroom and WC can be on the same floor to save steps. Ask the occupational therapist or social worker about these adaptations and grants to pay for them. Your mother may also qualify for a rent and rate rebate.

When the nursing becomes heavy, ask the GP to have your parent admitted to the geriatric unit at regular intervals, so you can have a rest and catch up on your sleep. Invoke all the supportive services available. If you co-operate with the district nurse, occupational therapist or anyone who comes into the case, your load will be substantially reduced. If the caring goes on for longer than two years, ask your parent to make adequate provision for you under the terms of her will. Many single people find themselves without a roof over their heads on the death of their parents (*see* Chapter Nine). If your mother is a council tenant, ask her to request the council to make you a joint tenant, with her, to protect your tenancy when your parent has died.

Somewhere in the back of your mind, you must remember that when your parent dies you will be left alone and you will have to cope with getting back into a normal life. If you prevent yourself from becoming too heavily overwhelmed by caring, you will have a much better chance of re-adapting more quickly.

In the event of your being no longer able to cope, you may have to allow your mother to be admitted to care (*see* Chapter Eight).

Getting off the work treadmill

There is a small minority of women who end up in the caring situation and who have been primarily motivated by a compulsion to get off the work treadmill. A typical woman in such a situation would be in her early forties, have been working since she was 18 or so, and have one or more of the following characteristics: her job is no longer very interesting, she has few friends, her housing seems unsatisfactory, and/or she cannot foresee an acceptable proposal of marriage. In such circumstances, she may be tempted to quit the world she has lived in for 20 or so years and now finds rather

18

boring, to return to the parental home with the avowed intention of caring for her frail but essentially (as yet) independent parent. Such a move could fill many gaps for her; she would escape the trials of employment, she would have a comfortable home, she would both receive and give affection within that home, and she would raise the possibility of making new friends in familiar surroundings. And so she will leave work to care full time.

It is possible, even probable, that the demands of the caring role will continually increase, and if she has not been motivated by a real need, a real sense of devotion or responsibility, or a vocation for caring, she could end up feeling wretched and caught in a web of her own weaving.

Your parent's being admitted to residential care

Many adult children find it almost impossible to come to terms with their mother's being admitted to residential care. They feel that they have let her down, or that they are being selfish and unkind. Yet in many instances, it is the only real solution for her. Some circumstances in which there may not be any other realistic alternative are these: that you are thirty, and your mother is confused and senile and could be so for another twenty years. You have never been compatible with her; or you are in mid-career and your parent has a seriously debilitating but not necessarily fatal disease. There are undoubtedly dozens of compelling reasons which could lead you to the decision that residential care is the answer. Finally, you should realize that you are under no legal obligation, whatever your sense of devotion or duty, to care for your parent.

Do not ignore the implications of any decision because you are concerned that your mother will feel rejected. If she loves you, she will, in her objective moments, want what is best for you and she will understand and accept the decision to place her in care. You should be aware that some illnesses could make her inclined to give her immediate needs first priority.

19

If it is agreed that your mother should be admitted to care, discuss what this will involve (I am assuming she is rational). Take her to see those places which have a vacancy, and as far as possible, let the final choice of place be hers. Go and inspect the rooms, talk to the matron, and see other people in there. Many homes are well organized and their residents happy and contented. If both your parents are living, try to ensure that the home chosen will take married couples, as undoubtedly they will want to be together when the time comes for both of them to be in care.

Despite a general inclination to identify residential care with the workhouse, the majority of authorities try to make residents feel that they are 'at home' by keeping rules to a minimum. Of course, your mother will be apprehensive, and even fearful, of leaving an established way of life to go into an unfamiliar environment, with unfamiliar schedules and faces; yet a positive attitude, a pre-awareness of the problems of residential living, plus your enthusiasm, can mentally prepare her for the transition and make the change easier to accept. As with boarding-school life, certain rules have to be adhered to: getting-up hours, meal times, retiring hours—they cannot be staggered as, if they were, staff and administrative problems would result.

Generally, your mother will be permitted to take her smaller items of furniture with her. As storage space is limited, usually it will not be possible for her to take every article of clothing she owns, and so she, or you on her behalf, will have to be selective.

Nowadays, there is more emphasis on the social aspect of life in homes and it is usual for concerts, cinema showings and some organized outings to feature in the lives of residents. Clergy visit, and religious services are held at least monthly in practically all homes.

After having lived as part of one's own family unit, communal living will not be easy to adapt to, yet there are definite advantages. Your mother will have company if she wants it, she will be properly fed and housed, there will be someone to keep an eye on her, she will not have the constant worry of housing maintenance or budgeting and, by and large, although one can feel lonely anywhere, she should not be as vulnerable to becoming an involuntary recluse.

Your contribution can be constructive—frequent contact with you will keep up her associations with her earlier life, and she won't feel abandoned by her family. You can take her on outings (according to her degree of mobility), have her home for holidays, keep her informed about other members of her family and friends, and help her to realize that she is still very much a part of the community.

THREE
General Home Nursing

Some knowledge of basic home nursing should be invaluable
to you. The district nurse will come in (your mother's GP will
arrange for her to do so) if your mother needs highly skilled
nursing. An auxiliary nurse can be sent in to bath her. If at all
possible, attend the British Red Cross Nursing Courses (*see*
Chapter Ten).

The ground rules of home nursing are to call a doctor if you
feel one is needed, and to consult him or the district nurse if
you are not sure about some change in symptoms, or how to
cope.

If your parent is bedbound and needs nursing attention,
try to be methodical—place everything you are going to need
on one tray. Make sure your hands are clean before you touch
any dressings, and dispose of soiled dressings promptly by
putting them into a disinfected covered receptacle. Scald out
bedpans, urinals, etc. after use. To prevent your parent from
developing bedsores turn her frequently. Use a 'sorbo' ring
or a sheepskin to fit under her buttocks so she will not have to
put up with pressure. A ripple bed can ease a much immob-
lized parent's discomfort.

You can borrow backrests, footrests, and bed cradles from
most Social Service Departments of your local authority.
Consult the district nurse about equipment to ease both the
impact of your parent's physical disability on her, and on
your nursing. In a bedbound or chairbound situation an
intercommunications system can be of tremendous help to
both of you. Ask the social worker to recommend a system.
The Call and Care Home Care Communication System is in
my opinion the best available. It is obtainable from Seton's
(*see* Chapter Ten).

Being disabled has psychological as well as physical disad-vantages. Nobody enjoys being dependent for her mobility or help with her bodily needs upon somebody else, despite their interrelationship.

Handling the handicapped requires considerable physical effort. If the 'art' of handling is understood, there will be less likelihood of strain in the handler.

Where possible the handler should use the handicapped person's weight to advantage. For instance, changing the position of an arm or a leg, or both, will change the weight distribution of the body.

Good movement and handling techniques should be understood and practised. It is essential to find out what limitations the handicapped person has, because of her dis-ability, and just how much help can be expected from her.

In every handling exercise careful assessment of the prob-lem, planning, and organizing how to deal with it should be gone through. The handicapped person must be encouraged to participate to the extent of her mental and physical capac-ity; not only will her co-operation help you, the carer, but it will boost her ego in that she won't feel so completely depen-dent.

When a handicapped person is being moved by the carer from one position to another, it is important that both should move together as one. There are various basic holds you should learn: the finger grip, the wrist grip, the through-arm lift grip, the armpit hold, the elbow grip, the pelvic holds, and various holds for adjusting the handicapped person's position.

Among what are known as the basic lifts are the orthodox lift, the shoulder lift, and modified shoulder lift, the elbow lift, through-arm lift, and the three-man lift.

The main functional activities with which the carer should be familiar are moving the disabled person to the side of the bed, turning her in bed, helping her to sit and move up the bed, helping her to sit on the side of the bed, getting her to stand up from a sitting position, sitting from standing up, from sitting to lying, to assist her with walking, to cross the floor to a chair, to cope with a wheelchair and stairs.

Where all the above methods of transfer have been tried and have failed, it may be necessary to use a mechanical hoist. A disabled person can be supplied with a hoist by her Social Services Department.

It may be necessary for a disabled parent to use a wheel-chair. There are many different chairs available, and if one is to be used permanently then it is essential to choose the right model. The type of chair that is needed should be discussed with the doctor and the therapist. Generally, where necessary, a chair will be provided free from the Red Cross, the local authority, or the Women's Royal Voluntary Services. There is a very useful pamphlet called *Handling the Handi-capped*, available from the Chartered Society of Physio-therapy, at 25p, which gives detailed instructions on how to use a wheelchair.

Where house alterations are indicated, the local authority Social Services department will send a qualified person to advise on ramps to cover steps.

BATHING

As regular bathing is an essential part of everyone's hygiene, you should make yourself familiar with some basic pointers which will make the job easier for you and more relaxing for your mother.

The majority of old people become upset at the thought of their children washing them all over; to them that means a loss of their last ounce of dignity. Therefore it is important that you, where at all possible, should encourage her to bath herself. If she can't climb in and out of a bath at least she may be able to have a 'bird bath'. If she is prone to dizzy turns, put a chair in front of the wash-basin so that she can sit down while she washes. A roller-towel fastened to the wall will enable her to dry her back and bottom more easily. An arthritic person may be greatly helped by taps fitted with a lever.

For more information on aids and adaptations, get yourself the book *Coping with Disablement* (available from the Consumer Association and most public libraries).

Using a cold bathroom is a rapid way for your mother to contract pneumonia. To avoid accidental scalding, always run the cold water before you run the hot. Have fresh clothes ready. After a bath is an appropriate time to attend to fingernails and toenails, since the warm water will have softened them. Where your mother's nails are too hard to manage yourself, get a chiropodist to cut them.

If your mother has to be bathed in bed, and the district nurse is not coming in to do this, get together all the equipment you are going to need before you start. Wash your mother a bit at a time, leaving the 'private parts' as they are commonly called, until last. If your mother can possibly cope with this area, leave her to get on with it; this will save you both unnecessary embarrassment.

If she is incontinent, special care should be taken to bathe your mother's buttocks frequently. If chafing and stinging are to be lessened, thorough washing, application of a barrier cream and clean linen and clothing are a 'must' for incontinent people. Keep an alert eye for pressure sores—because their neglect can cause severe discomfort.

DAILY CARE OF THE TEETH, TONGUE, MOUTH, AND HAIR

It is essential to see that your mother's teeth, tongue, and mouth are kept clean. If she has dentures, provide a tumbler of water containing a denture-cleaning powder for them overnight. The district nurse will tell you what solution to mix up to remove furry coverings from her mouth and tongue.

Well-combed, brushed, and clean hair does a lot for the ego, particularly if your mother is a vain elderly lady! It may be possible for a hairdresser to come in once a month; or if your mother is a senior citizen and mobile she will probably be able to have her hair done at the hairdressers' at a reduced rate.

Keep your own hair in good condition and well groomed.

MAKING A BED

If possible, place your mother's bed where she can look out on the world if she wants to.

In making a bed quickly and easily you should have all the linen and other articles you need on a table or chair near the bed, with a plastic bag ready for the soiled linen. You should wipe down any rubber or polythene sheeting daily with a disinfectant solution. Remember to check that the under-sheet is free of creases.

TAKING THE PULSE

The district nurse will show you how to take your parent's pulse. The rhythmic beat (it is rhythmic in a healthy person) indicates the rate of the heart beat. For most people, the pulse rate is around 72 beats a minute. There are variations either side of this figure. Ask the district nurse or GP to check what your mother's usual rate is, so that you will have some guide. Use a watch with a seconds hand to get an accurate reading. If your parent has been exercising, is upset, or has an infection, the rate will be affected.

TEMPERATURE—HOW TO TAKE IT

When taking your mother's temperature, you should know that it can be taken in the mouth for one minute, under the arm for four minutes, or in the rectum (bottom) for two minutes. You must first shake the thermometer so that it registers less than 35 °C (94·5 °F) before insertion. To do this, hold the thermometer firmly between your thumb and forefinger at the end opposite to that where the mercury bulb is, and shake it vigorously with a sharp, snapping movement.

Reading a thermometer is not difficult. As most are more

or less triangular in shape, one edge is normally more pointed than the others. You should have that sharp edge facing you. In this position, the markings on the thermometer should be visible. The degrees are signified by the lines above those of the number. Between them is the vacuum tube through which the mercury flows. Turn the thermometer so that you can see the mercury. The place where the mercury ends is where you must look to read your mother's temperature.

Most thermometers are labelled in much the same way. A long mark for each degree and a short mark for each one-tenth of a degree. An arrow points to the 'normal' mark.

Be sure to leave the thermometer in place for the required time. Do not take your mother's temperature after a hot or cold drink or a bath. The best time of day to take it is in the early morning or the late afternoon, as the symptoms of most people's illnesses worsen in the evening. It is essential to realize that your mother is not necessarily ill simply because the temperature does not remain constant at normal. Everyone's temperature rises and falls according to the time of day and the physical movement.

In the interests of hygiene remember to wash the thermometer after use.

MEDICINES

Keep all medicines, except those that have to be taken in an emergency, out of your mother's reach. Double check before you give any medicine that it is the right bottle or phial, and that the dosage is right.

We all know that drugs can produce side effects, and some more than others. Do not leave a question about a drug unanswered, merely because you believe the doctor will consider you foolish. Therefore make sure you understand the following: what the drug is prescribed for; whether there will be any adverse side-effects; what dosage should be taken; how frequently it should be taken; whether it should be taken before meals, after meals, or during meals; whether

27

some foods cause the drug to have an adverse side-effect; whether alcohol can safely be consumed during the period the drug is being taken; whether a particular drug can be safely taken with others—for instance, whether it is advisable to take aspirin while taking the drug.

The pharmacist knows about drugs, and therefore you can safely ask him any of these questions.

PRESCRIPTIONS

Know what time your pharmacy opens and closes and what arrangements are made for emergency prescriptions.

Prescriptions are free if your mother is 60 or more (65 if it is your father). Every prescription form has a 'box' on the back of it. Your mother should put a tick in this box and sign the form in the space provided.

If your mother is a hospital outpatient, and is 60 or more, (65 if it is your father) then drugs obtained at the hospital dispensary are free.

Do not be a 'doctor haunter' over simple health problems, but do not neglect to ask about important aspects of caring. There are some reliable home remedies. (See *Take Care of Yourself*, in Recommended Further Reading).

ENEMAS

Some knowledge of enemas, etc. may prove helpful. Elderly people sometimes need to relieve constipation with an enema treatment. Constipation can cause discomfort, a sick sensation, and overall it is not good for the general health. If your mother needs an enema, ask the district nurse to show you how to apply it the first time. If you live in an isolated area and cannot easily get in touch with the district nurse, do not panic, but follow this simple procedure: place a waterproof sheet and a towel under your mother's buttocks. Roll her onto her side, have a pre-filled enema at hand. Gently insert the nozzle into the rectum (Vaseline on the tip helps) and then release the fluid. Ask her to retain the fluid as long as possible. Usually there is no reaction for several minutes.

Have the bedpan or commode, cottonwool and toilet tissue ready for use.

Some GPs prescribe suppositories to relieve constipation. These are made of gelatine or wax and contain drugs which stimulate the bowel action, after they have been pushed up into the rectum.

For good, safe toilet hygiene, make sure all equipment is very clean. Check that it is safe to use an enema on her.

DIET

If your mother is on a special diet, do not make any changes without consulting her doctor. Maintaining a variety of foods (where medically permissible) in your mother's diet, should encourage her to eat more. Aroma, taste and flavour all stimulate the proper secretion of digestive juices, which change the food we eat into body-building material.

If your parent eats slowly, and her food tends to get cold, buy a hot plate (about £9) which is hot only where the dinner-plate sits, so that her food will stay warm. A two-handled feeding-cup is also useful in encouraging independence in a very infirm old person. Send to the Disabled Living Foundation (see Chapter Ten) for information on aids to enable her to feed herself without undue difficulty.

If she is so infirm that you must feed her, do not try to do so while she is lying down, as she could choke.

You, too, must eat properly. Don't skimp your meals because she is constantly calling you, set aside a definite meal period and do your best to keep it.

The menus set out below have been evolved only as a guide. It is in no way suggested that you should follow them slavishly. It may not always be convenient or possible to obtain or serve specific foods on the list, or alternatively, some food may not be popular in your house.

A well-balanced diet is necessary, and to achieve it, you must daily eat a certain quantity of the 'basic' foods—fruit, vegetables, cereals, milk, cheese, eggs, and meat. The given menus are calculated to provide such a diet.

BREAKFAST	LUNCH	DINNER

Monday

Sliced fruit and wheat germ	Tomato salad	Vegetable soup
scrambled egg	scones	curry from Sunday's
toast/honey	baked custard (using 2	joint
milk, tea, coffee	egg whites only of 3	rice/vegetable
	whole eggs)	banana custard
	milk, tea, coffee	milk, tea, coffee

Tuesday

Potato cakes	Cheese omelette	Minced steak pie (buy
bacon	bread, butter	1 lb)
toast/marmalade	fresh fruit	beans, potatoes
milk, tea, coffee	milk, tea, coffee	jam roll
		milk, tea, coffee

Wednesday

Porridge	Macaroni cheese	Celery soup
grilled tomatoes on toast	stewed fruit	stuffed marrow
milk, tea, coffee	milk, tea, coffee	(using other half pound of steak)
		fruit salad
		milk, tea, coffee

Thursday

Stewed prunes	Grilled sausage and salad	Irish stew
boiled egg	fresh fruit or queen's	potatoes, peas
toast	pudding (using egg	berries if in season or
milk, tea, coffee	white from Monday	cake
	for topping)	milk, tea, coffee
	milk, tea, coffee	

Friday

Orange juice
bacon
toast
milk, tea, coffee

Salad with grated
   cheese
scones (left over pud-
   ding)
apple
milk, tea, coffee

Sausage meat loaf
potatoes, beans
marrow (left over from
   Wednesday)
baked rice custard
milk, tea, coffee

Saturday

Fruit, stewed or fresh
toast and honey,
milk, tea, coffee

Coleslaw and toasted
   peanut butter
   sandwich
cake, orange
milk, tea, coffee

Bacon and egg
potatoes, peas
stewed apples and cus-
   tard
milk, tea, coffee

Sunday

Grapefruit
toast, egg
milk, tea, coffee

Soup
roast stuffed veal or
   roast chicken
baked potatoes, 2 veg.
apple pie
milk, tea, coffee

Sardines on toast or
   ham salad
cake, fruit salad
milk, tea, coffee

EXERCISE

Physical activity aids good health. In particular, exercise has been shown to benefit people with digestive problems, muscle problems, poor respiration and poor circulation.

To maintain your mother's health you may try to prevent her from exerting herself, but in so doing you may be over-protective, and your over-protectiveness could lead to her premature death. As far as possible, try not to restrict her activities but rather encourage them. You, too, should see that you get enough exercise.

Psychologically, being confined to any limited area can be depressing; while going out, even with difficulty, can be very beneficial.

Gardening can be a very gentle form of exercise. If your mother has been a keen gardener and she can still get about and bend, encourage her to keep on with it. The advantages of this particular activity are that it provides varied movements, takes her out in the fresh air and is psychologically rewarding.

SLEEPING

Ageing can bring changes in sleeping patterns. Few elderly people can hope to sleep soundly the whole night through; sometimes they will wake several times, and stay awake for varying and possibly protracted periods.

Presumably you are fully occupied either from working and caring, or from full-time caring, and you cannot afford any sustained interference with your rest. Therefore, you should plan your mother's night as carefully as you can, with the objective that her wakefulness will not affect you.

Check that her room is at a comfortable temperature, that she has a comfortable (firm, if at all possible) bed and that the bedclothes are adequate. Warm milk may relax her when she is lying awake for a long time, so leave a thermos flask of warm milk on the bedside table. The late-night radio can take her mind off her sleeplessness, and if she wears earphones the radio won't disturb you. Reading is a renowned soporific, so if she enjoys reading, you should ensure that she has books at hand and an adequate reading lamp by the bed.

Where she is awake for hours and becomes anxious and depressed about it, tell her GP. He may either prescribe a sleeping-pill, or check on her general well-being to ensure that her restlessness is not the indication of some disease. He may do both.

Before a bedbound parent goes to sleep, brush any crumbs off the bed, puff up the pillows, make sure the room is at an even temperature, get her to use the bed-pan and wash her hands afterwards. Close the curtains, make sure the Care and Call is close at hand in case she needs to rouse you in the night, and give her a drink of whatever beverage she likes. If she is incontinent the doctor may recommend that she drinks only a little before retiring.

OVERALL ORGANIZATION AND A CONTENTED ATMOSPHERE

If you are to cope, it is essential for you to organize your daily schedule. Lack of organization can produce impatience and an unsettled feeling in your mother, frustration and fatigue in you. Equally, of course, too rigid a schedule can cause tension and anxiety in you both. It is advisable to strive for a flexible routine within a well-defined framework.

As far as your parent's particular needs will permit, endeavour to approach your caring responsibilities on the basis of a time-and-motion study. This means that you should make the maximum use of every ounce of energy invested.

A system will prevent overlap and duplication. At nursing level have a schedule. At housekeeping level, invest in as many labour-saving devices as you can afford; don't dry the dishes, put them on a plastic drainer; soak unclean clothes, don't scrub at them; if at all possible use paper handkerchiefs; don't iron nightwear except perhaps the collars; cover your kitchen shelves with self-adhesive plastic which will wipe clean easily; if you can afford them, buy non-stick pans; try to put everything back where it belongs after use; bake a cake and a casserole at the same time; keep dusters and cleaning materials together.

When you get home (presuming you work), try to have a rest before you start with the chores. As far as you can, keep to the essentials—the hand-basin, the sink, the kitchen floor, the toilet and removal of rubbish. It will save much more time and energy if you make one full swoop in a marathon effort.

A well-thought-out plan will give you more time to yourself.

Helping time to pass quickly is as important in home nursing as changing the bed linen.

For an invalid parent stimulating interests are life-lines; she will tend to remain mentally alert longer, be more contented, and feel less of a burden, if she pursues some definite interests. Reading can open up new and varied vistas, and your library tokens will entitle you to a wide choice of books.

Games such as monopoly, cards, scrabble, etc. are relaxing and yet present a certain amount of challenge.

Music is very therapeutic. Television and radio programmes can fill many hours. Some old persons (and for that matter, young persons) tend to identify with television personalities.

Use of earphones will prevent the non-participating person from being disturbed.

Knitting, embroidery, sewing, and so on are all satisfying crafts, and faculties still permitting, one can learn them at any age. One old lady acquaintance went to dress-making classes at 75, and at 85 still makes her own dresses!

Of course one has to be motivated. For your part, your motivation should be to find a channel for some self-expression. If you spend 24 hours a day caring, then it must be that you haven't invoked the available services, or your parent should be in a geriatric ward, or you are poorly

34

organized, or you are parent-dominated to an alarming degree.

The common complaints of old age

The most common complaints you could have to cope with in your elderly parent could be her immobility, her instability (loss of balance or proneness to falling), her incontinence, and her impaired intellectual ability.

There is a profusion of equipment to help cope with her immobility. Improvements such as handrails on the stairs and bath, etc. will help her if she is inclined to fall; incontinence can generally be treated if caught in time and better equipment is now available to alleviate some of her embarrassment and your work; and if you can be patient yet not over-indulgent of her decreasing mental faculty you will have an easier time if she is becoming confused.

Some old people tend to neglect their eyes, hearing and teeth, therefore I have briefly described how you can encourage your parent to seek medical advice if necessary.

The risk of hypothermia and accidents can essentially be reduced if the carer is alerted to their causes.

IMMOBILITY

Your parent's immobility can produce serious depression which may be manifested in feelings of 'giving up' and, of course, if this occurs, your job as carer will be more onerous.

There are numerous medical causes of immobility; among which are stroke aftermath, arthritis, severe heart conditions, terminal cancer, or sometimes sore feet. Sadly some medical conditions are accompanied by pain and for some patients every movement can produce severe discomfort if not excruciating pain.

Nowadays, however, most painful conditions at least can be made bearable by drugs, and your mother should not try to cope using some 'family cure'. At the outset of any debilitating condition she should consult her doctor. If necessary he will send the district nurse who will advise her on what home treatments can be carried out and on what equipment is available to give her as much comfort and independence as possible. Perhaps the physio-therapist will work with her to help her to get some mobility back into her legs or arms and hands. The physio-therapist is the best judge of how mobile your mother should be, and according to her guidance it is vital for you to encourage your parent to be as mobile as possible. The domiciliary occupational therapist can arrange if necessary for handrails to be installed on both sides of any stairs, and where needed she can see that your parent's bed or chair is lifted to a manageable height.

It is important for you to encourage your parent to co-operate with the professionals for two very good reasons; she will be less likely to be depressed and you will not be so much in demand.

For helpful information and advice and practical aid for arthritic patients, write to the British Rheumatism and Arthritis Association for their excellent brochure.

For helpful information on helping a stroke patient write to the Chest Heart and Stroke Association, for their first-class brochure on these disabilities.

If your parent has cancer and it is in the terminal stage, write to the Marie Curie Memorial Foundation (for addresses see Chapter Ten).

Certain house adaptations can be made to help a disabled person to cope more satisfactorily (*see* Chapter Seven).

Again may I emphasize that an inter-communications system will help her to feel less isolated if she is bedbound or chairbound, and your energy should be saved too.

INCONTINENCE

Incontinence is a condition in which a person is unable to control her bladder or bowels. Double incontinence (that is, where neither the bladder nor the bowels can be controlled) is one of the most embarrassing of human predicaments, and without use of the aids which are available, the caring situation it produces can become intolerable.

What should be recognized by all elderly people and those caring for them is that incontinence is not caused by old age. It is attributable to any one of a number of causes, and any first sign of the problem should be thoroughly investigated by an old person's GP. Among the factors which can perhaps promote a tendency towards incontinence are immobility or difficulty in moving about. An old person may have a sudden urge to empty her bladder but be unable to get to the toilet in time. An arthritic person or stroke victim, or someone using a Zimmer frame, could find themselves in this situation. Of course, the simple answer is to have a commode (and there are now furniture-like commodes) in the room where the patient usually is, or to have the cause of immobility removed or made less burdensome by such a process as hip surgery.

Another factor affecting a normal body function is mental vagueness. The urge to go to the toilet may come, but the old person may immediately forget about it, and before she can attend to it, she wets her pants. Again, her GP may be able to prescribe a drug, give her vitamins, or use some therapy to improve her mental condition and, at secondary level, remove her distressing condition of incontinence.

The bladder itself may not work properly, perhaps there is a slight non-serious blockage or sometimes an instrument merely has to be inserted in the mouth of the bladder to open it up more and the incontinence problem will be solved. Carers should always approach the problem of incontinence on the basis that the condition is not the fault of the old person.

The proper equipment for those who are in fact incontinent is very important. The types of help available fall under three headings:

> aids and equipment
> laundry service
> waste-disposal service

(Note that the availability of the above services varies from one area to another.)

Aids and Equipment

Recently there has been considerable advance made in the design and efficiency of aids and equipment. Before any personal investment is made in it, however, the area health authority in your region should be approached, as they often supply a range of equipment such as a commode on loan (which is not easily deodorized) or bed linen (some have supplies of disposable sheets), interliners, incontinence pads (for example, Kanga pads, Cumfies, Inco) and protective pants. There are lightweight polythene or polypropylene urinals for both men and women. Details of suppliers of all the above and various types of equipment can be obtained from the Disabled Living Foundation, at a small charge of around 30p, or usually from the district nurse.

There are raised toilet seats for persons with arthritic hips, and bars that can be fixed to the wall beside the toilet to give the old person support in settling on to and getting off the toilet. A raised toilet seat can be obtained from the local authority domiciliary occupational therapy service.

Then there is the Kylie product, a highly absorbent sheet, which absorbs a very large amount of urine without the surface becoming too wet or an odour developing. It can be put on at night and not taken off till next morning, when it can be laundered in a domestic washing machine, then tumble-dried. Details can be obtained from the suppliers, Nicholas Laboratories, P.O. Box 17, 225 Bath Road, Slough, Berkshire. There are, of course, other such products, and again, details can be obtained from the Disabled Living Foundation.

Laundry Service

Many local authorities supply a laundry service, and you should not hesitate to make use of it.

Disposal of Waste

Generally the local Environmental Health Department provides a refuse disposal service. This service collects soiled incontinence pads (and sick-room waste).

Initially, you should enquire about any of the above services and equipment from your mother's GP.

An elderly incontinent person may take some persuading to use the aids, but they are comfortable and mean less overall changing.

If your mother is incontinent, a lot of embarrassing changing of clothes can be prevented by using easy-to-change wear. For further information, contact the Women's Royal Voluntary Service, who supply a booklet on sewing such clothing. Easily opened garments will also enable you to keep your parent well bathed and powdered. A major cause of chafing and bedsores is being left in clothing soaked with urine or faeces.

If you care for your mother at home, and she receives supplementary pension, and if extra money has to be spent on her laundry because of incontinence, then the actual cost over 10p a week incurred may be additionally claimed.

MENTAL CONFUSION

As their present life is generally so uneventful, so unexciting and so bereft of close friends, many old people begin to dwell in the past. Often, their conversation is dominated by 'What I did when I was young' or 'how much better life was forty years ago'.

Nothing could be more natural an escape from a dull, uninteresting present, and such behaviour shouldn't be hastily interpreted as an indication of the onset of senility. Indeed confusion is often the result of some physical illness, and once the illness is cured the confusion will go. So if the confusion suddenly occurs do see the GP.

Forgetfulness in old age doesn't necessarily indicate mental confusion either. Only where the trait seems to be becoming progressively worse, or your mother's failing memory is endangering her person, other people or

39

property, should you think about taking constructive steps to have it investigated.

Of course, some old people do suffer from mental illness (as can any of us at any time). Bereavement, frustration, boredom and isolation can all make an old person more vulnerable to mental infirmity. Foibles which have been hidden during a lifetime, when it was essential to function as a well-adjusted member of society, may suddenly become apparent. If you analyse what appear to be sudden changes in her personality, you may realize that there have always been hints of such behaviour; the difference being that they are now more evident or prominent.

Your mother's GP should be able to diagnose your mother's real condition. Some forms of mental illness can be effectively treated; among them are depression and neuroses.

Senile dementia, the decay of the mind due to the organic degeneration of parts of the brain, cannot be cured.

If your mother does develop senile dementia, you will need all the strength and will power in the world to cope. It would not be untrue to state that it is a wearying disease to live with; the constant repetitiveness, the inability to remember longer than a minute or two, time disorientation, all put terrible strains on the one taking care of the ill person.

As one carer said,

Mother became confused—she called non-stop twenty-four hours a day. I kept running to her. I ended up having a breakdown. I know now it wouldn't have been unkind to have ignored most of her calling. If only we could know about these things in advance; but we aren't trained to take care of the elderly, are we?

Your mother's GP may require her to be admitted to an old people's psychiatric ward for a few days so she can be more closely observed. If this is necessary, reassure her that it will be for only a short period. One of the most tragic aspects of this disease is that the sufferer often has some lucid moments.

A symptom of mental illness can be a continuous restlessness at night. This can result in your getting too little sleep. Sleeplessness plus anxiety may combine to produce a feeling of perpetual weariness. It is essential for you to get as much relief as possible. As mentioned earlier, the Care and Call Home Care System from Seton's will help you; it 'tells' you when someone is out of bed (*see* Chapter Ten). The GP may assist you by prescribing medication for your mother.

Another type of mental problem in the elderly is mental delusions. These delusions may, for example, manifest themselves in accusations against a son or daughter of ill treatment, or of theft of personal belongings, etc. It can be very embarrassing if the delusions are attached to a neighbour's or friend's behaviour. As far as is humanly possible, try to pass off such behaviour as a symptom of illness. Explain your parent's condition to any outsider who is maligned—an understanding person will shrug off unfounded accusations; for the others, don't be unduly distressed by their narrow perspectives (or small-mindedness)! Where this problem is not too far advanced, it can often be helped by your saying to your parent, 'Where did you put my purse?' she will generally be aghast at your innuendo and for a while will not indulge in her own accusations.

Mental confusion by its very nature often leads to a more intense interdependent relationship. Many carers do everything they can to conceal their parent's condition from the doctor, from any other professional with whom they have contact, and from people generally. Those who have this medieval attitude seldom leave their confused parent. And sooner or later the strain of this closeness will tell.

If you decide to continue to care for your mentally confused parent, you may be fortunate enough to live in an area where you will receive help from the district nurse, possibly a home help, regular visits from a health visitor and, if requested, by a GP, from a social worker, and there may be a

41

Day Centre for the confused. This will be your network of support, but it can function only if you yourself ask for help.

Caring for an old person who is mentally confused can be more wearying than any other job. Periodically, it will be essential for you to get away. Ask for help. Your mother's GP should be able to arrange for her temporary admission to hospital or to an old people's home. The social services may say that she is too disturbed for one of their old people's homes, but the GP should be able to use his influence for her, and persuade one of the services to accept her.

Several authorities have Day Centres exclusively for the mentally infirm. Day care can give you some respite. However, the question of transporting your mother to and from the Centre may give you second thoughts about using this amenity, even if it is available.

Some community doctors make night sitters-in available for persons with a confused elderly relative. This service is provided by a statutory body. If it is available, make use of it. Night disturbance is often a major factor in the breakdown of the carer's health.

Day hospitals are available in some areas. Where they do exist, their function is social relief and support of the patient's family, and they provide appropriate psychiatric treatment without recourse to hospital admission.

There are those carers who just cannot cope with this situation. Their own health is put in jeopardy and they feel trapped. It is not unusual for someone under severe pressure to react by bullying or physically assaulting an old person. Perhaps such a reaction can be understood, but it is reprehensible on a carer's part not to seek professional help when she recognizes that she is reaching this stage. The health visitor, the district nurse, the social worker, the doctor, the vicar, an Age Concern organizer, will all offer constructive advice. To protect your own mental stability, they may advise admitting your parent to a geriatric ward for a couple of weeks. While she is there, the GP may experiment with drugs to see which one, if any, will help her condition. Sometimes tests will reveal that the confusion is due to a disease which, if treated properly, will cause the side effect, mental confusion, to abate.

It could happen that your mother's condition cannot be cured or even alleviated and that you just cannot be responsible for her any longer. Admission to geriatric or mental institutional care or to hospital on a permanent basis may be the only solution to an intolerable situation.

The Social Services Department could react by saying they have no suitable accommodation for someone so much disturbed, and the psychiatric hospital may report that she is not disturbed enough for long-term admission. But here the problem becomes your GP's battle.

After your mother's admission, you may experience guilt, overwhelming feelings of loss and uselessness, and doubts as to the quality of care your mother may receive. Remind yourself that your stable mother would never have wanted you to be burdened with her impossible condition. Allowing her to go into care doesn't reflect in any way upon your sense of devotion and duty. It is merely the realistic solution to a very difficult problem.

Some hospitals do try hard to improve the quality of life for the more mentally alert—patients are treated as normal as far as staff and facilities permit.

On the other hand, homes seldom offer occupational therapy and little stimulation through communication. The situation will undoubtedly distress you, but you must rationalize it as your only course of action. Don't allow any remorse syndrome on your part to upset your mother, by your exclamations of how inferior care in that home is. If you project a positive, cheerful approach, your mother's lucid moments should be happier.

You should know about some of the legal implications of your parent's becoming incapable of managing her own affairs.

The Court of Protection exists to protect the property of a

person who is incapable of managing her own affairs because of mental disorder.

Applications for the appointment of a receiver may be made to the Court by any person either by instructing a solicitor to carry through this application, or with the assistance of the Personal Branch of the Court. The address of the Court of Protection is: The Chief Clerk, Court of Protection, 25 Store Street, London WC1E 7BP.

Where an application has been made to the Court, there is a statutory requirement that notice should be sent to the patient telling her of the application, and of the name and address of the person applying, and informing her of the date on which the application is to be heard.

Assuming that a receiver is appointed, he will need to submit an annual account of dealings with the patient's property to the Court.

Where the patient recovers, and can produce substantiating medical evidence of the fact of recovery, she may apply for the discharge of the receiver.

A note of caution to the unscrupulous relative who has been appointed receiver—any professional involved in your mentally incapable parent's case may apply to the Court for moneys to be released to meet your parent's needs.

EYES

When you suspect that your mother's eyesight is deteriorating, encourage her to go, or take her, to the doctor. If the GP decides that an appointment with an ophthalmologist is necessary, he will refer her.

Usually, you will find that all your mother needs are glasses or a change of glasses. In the rare event of the ophthalmologist's having to certify her as blind or partially sighted, he will send such certification to the Social Services department. If your mother is placed on the Blind Registry, she will receive a visit from the social worker.

Those who are blind are eligible for

The British Talking Book Service for the Blind (at Mount Pleasant, Alperton, Middlesex)

Visual aids, such as magnifiers

Mobility Aids; a white stick or a guide dog to help her move about more easily

Nowadays a blind person is not relegated to a lonely, dark world—medical care and aids can improve the quality of life for many poor-sighted people. Do not be one of those people who shrug off blindness or poor sight in the aged as something to be expected.

HEARING

The quality of life of an aged person is much better if she can hear well. The elderly are often very reluctant to have a hearing aid, either because they believe that to admit to being deaf is to admit to 'going down hill', or because someone they know has reported that hearing aids are terrible gadgets to wear. It cannot be denied that some hearing aids do cause problems. However, with care, they can generally be adjusted quite satisfactorily.

If you suspect that your mother is having difficulty with her hearing, ask the GP to check it. He will examine her ears to try to determine whether or not the deafness is due to some wax build-up or other easily remedied reason, or simply old age. If he can't find the cause for the deafness, he'll refer you to the Ear Nose and Throat Department at the hospital.

National Health Service hearing aids are given free, on prescription, by the consultant who sees your mother; repairs and batteries are also free. The National Health Service behind-the-ear aids are becoming much more readily available now. If your mother wants to buy an aid privately, advice can be obtained from the Royal National Institute for the Dead (*see* Chapter Ten).

TEETH

No one can properly digest poorly chewed food, and the aged are no exception. Encourage your mother to have her teeth checked periodically. Decayed teeth or diseased gums can cause misery and affect disposition and general health.

If your mother wears dentures, it is essential to have them changed at regular intervals because her gums will shrink. Improperly fitting dentures can cause serious problems; for instance, mouth cancer can result from the prolonged rubbing of a denture on a particular place in the mouth.

If your mother gets a supplementary pension or has a low income, false teeth and other dental treatments are free. Ask her dentist for the FID form. Fill this in to ensure against paying on a private-fee basis. In fact, before any treatment begins, establish quite definitely that the dentist appreciates that he is treating your mother under the National Health Service. Where she is not on Supplementary Benefit, or hasn't a low income, only a small fee is payable.

It is worth noting that dentures and dental treatment are free while your mother is in hospital. Arrangements can be made for a dentist to visit your mother at home where a visit is necessary. No extra charge will be made. Your mother's GP will arrange such a visit.

HYPOTHERMIA

Elderly people often either keep the temperature of their homes too high and unnecessarily burn up fuel, or they tend to save on fuel to a dangerous level, and run a definite risk of hypothermia.

If your mother is coping alone, check on the kind of heating used, that there is adequate ventilation, that proper insulation has been installed, and above all, that she has a sensible attitude to the question of the level of heat. A large house is harder to heat than a small one. If your mother is in a big family home persuade her to close off some of the rooms so that heat will not be pumped needlessly into unoccupied space.

The elderly are particularly vulnerable to hypothermia because their temperature sense has become less acute and because their bodies may tend to cool uniformly and not react to the cold in the normal manner with preferential cooling of the hands and extremities. This happens if the part of their brain which 'registers' heat changes is not functioning properly. Again, some old people totally lose their ability to recognize that the air around them is cold, that their body temperature has dropped, and that they must make an effort to get warm.

Hypothermia can be fatal.

If you find your mother generally cold and ill, in a very cold room, check the skin temperature of her tummy. If that is cold to the touch, there is a good chance that she is suffering from hypothermia. Call her GP at once.

While you are waiting for him to come, warm the room generally. It is dangerous to direct heat at her. Give her warm drinks and put more clothes on her.

If your mother can't move about easily or suffers from arthritis, heart disease, bronchitis, or rheumatism, particular care must be taken not to let her get cold. You should be on the alert if you notice that your mother does not complain about feeling cold when you do, and if she does not shiver when she might reasonably be expected to do so (*see* Chapter Seven).

ACCIDENTS AND INSTABILITY

Many elderly persons end up disabled as a result of an accident within the home. Elderly women are particularly prone to falling. Although there can be several medical causes for instability, such as diseases where dizziness is a symptom, poor eyesight, your parent can usually be safeguarded from the impact of falling by some common-sense actions. It is essential therefore, that every preventive measure be taken to ensure that the home is as safe as possible.

The most common causes of accidents are lack of rails on

the bath, wet and/or slippery floors, uneven floor surfaces, torn floor coverings, objects left carelessly on the floor, any of which can cause an old person to trip; furniture with sharp corners placed where frail hip-joints may bump into them and cause fractures; faulty and damaged equipment; poor lighting over the stairs and steps (particularly at night); lack of two railings on stairs; essential gadgets in cupboards which can be reached only by steps; and improperly guarded fires.

Try to avoid accidents by anticipating them; of course, that doesn't mean that you should become neurotic about potentially hazardous conditions—just take reasonable care. Constructive steps you can take to make a home less accident prone are such things as sticking a strip of shiny white tape along the outside edge of the top and bottom steps on stairs; having a second banister put up to give added support; having a stair lift put in (if your parent has a heart condition)—the local authority may help with the cost; affixing handrails to baths and to the wall beside the toilet seat.

This list is by no means exhaustive, but it should identify the most common accident traps and preventive measures. The Royal Society for the Prevention of Accidents has available, at a small cost, a series of leaflets and booklets on aspects of home safety of which you should be aware.

FOUR
The Emotional Aspects of Caring

Inevitably caring produces a very close relationship in which the dependant and the carer could become interdependent and unless every effort is made to preserve individuality, an unhappy situation can arise.

At the time that many people assume the caring role they are inclined to organize their lives and their attitudes on the basis that the aged person may not have a long life expectancy, and they tend to become slaves to her every whim. What they are subconsciously doing is satisfying themselves that they have given the best care that they can, and on her death they won't have any feelings of neglect or remorse. But caring can stretch into twenty or thirty years, and once a pattern has been set, it can be virtually impossible to break it. Therefore caring should be approached on the basis that it could be long term.

Let us examine the impact on your mother of becoming dependent on you. It is of the utmost importance to encourage independence for as long as possible. You can do this by not putting her into the useless, helpless role where she has to feel a nuisance. Perhaps it will take her half an hour to shuffle from the back door to a seat in the garden, but let her do it. Getting there is very important to her. Many single carers lavish unnecessary attention and protection on their disabled parents making paper dolls of them, but paper dolls crush and go limp quickly and so will your mother. Restrain yourself from treating her as the child you never had. It is true that disability can produce a fear of the future and loss of confidence, but a positive attitude on your part can restore a lot of confidence, however dreary the real prospects.

We are taught that all of us should contribute to society and this premise does not change at the age of 65. As far as your parent's disability will allow, delegate as much of your

49

overall household responsibility as possible. The menu-planning, the dusting, the vegetable-peeling, the cake-icing, flower-arranging, cleaning the silver, folding the clothes, ironing handkerchiefs, tidying the cutlery drawer, and many other light chores are all essential parts of housekeeping; and her performance of some of them will give her satisfaction and remove some of the burden from your shoulders.

Although you may have sacrificed your independence, your mother will invariably show greater affection towards your brothers and sisters, who probably visit irregularly, who are quite unhelpful, and have little or no time in their lives for her. After their visits you probably will have to hear their praises sung; you will be subjected to painful comparisons, and ultimately you will probably be left an equal share with them in her will. She may tell you that Joyce looks so young, so well and so successful, while you, on the other hand, should do something about your appearance. You will be hurt, but if you can interpret her attitude as typical, it should be less distressing.

At such a time it will be perfectly natural for you to feel resentful of your married brothers' and sisters' relative freedom, their material possessions and ability to pursue their own lives. You will probably feel guilty about your resentment and this may build up tensions in an already strained situation.

When you first become involved in the caring process, you should be aware that there are some elderly people for whom the more is done, the more possessive and demanding they become. Many of them use what can be labelled 'emotional blackmail'. Let me give you an example of this subtle weaponry.

Jill M. had an eighty-year-old, infirm mother, for whom she had been caring for five years. The strain was telling on Jill's health and her doctor had advised her to get at least one day's respite a week. Jill's cousin had offered to 'mother-sit' for Jill, while she went to meet an old friend.

Quite properly, Jill told her mother a couple of days before her proposed outing. The old lady became very agitated, she refused to eat and complained of pains in her stomach. The doctor came and told Jill that as far as he could determine, there was no medical reason for this condition. After he left, Mrs M. began to cry and told Jill that if she left her, she might die. Jill was upset because she realized her mother was being selfish, yet she was afraid to run the risk of her dying, or even really falling ill, if she did leave her. The idea of carrying such guilt for the rest of her life was unthinkable. She rang her friend, apologized, and cancelled her outing.

Mrs M. had successfully used emotional blackmail. If Jill M. had deliberately tried to retain her identity and independence from the beginning, the situation cited should never have arisen.

Many carers set the scene for such behaviour, because through unfamiliarity with the caring role they tend to over-indulge their infirm parents at the expense of their own health and happiness.

Each of you is an individual, and you must take steps to preserve your own individuality. Don't fall into a pattern that allows no escape for you. If your parent begins to use emotional blackmail, remind her that you could collapse yourself if you don't get some respite.

Aggression, ill-temper and petulance can be forms of weaponry through which some old people make unreasonable demands on their carers and effectively intimidate them.

When an elderly parent has been the fiercely dominant member of the household, she will not readily abdicate that role despite her disability and consequent dependence on her adult child. You can be sure that 'once a tyrant, always a tyrant'. Equally somebody who has always been a family 'dogsbody' may bask in the attention the family shower on her and deliberately affect a particular brand of helplessness.

A daughter who has always been easily dominated can become a virtual slave to an aggressive parent's whims, and unless she firmly asserts herself the pattern will not improve—it will, in fact, get worse.

Quite often an old person can cleverly adopt a Dr-Jekyll-and-Mr-Hyde character, and the casual outsider will not believe that the daughter's existence is made virtually intolerable. Alternatively, some old parents are dominated by their daughters, and they lead the most miserable of lives. If they are completely dependent on the daughter, they are too much afraid of the consequences to voice any complaint to callers.

Possessiveness has to be guarded against in every caring relationship.

Your mother may selfishly try to dominate your time, your attention and your affection. She can feel jealous of anyone else's coming in, or of any other demands on your time and energies. In severe cases, she can insist on your sleeping in her room, or even in her bed.

A possessive, selfish parent is an unnecessary burden, and perpetually you will have to fight off any tendency to give in to her. That means you will have to be self-assertive. Often this will cause tension and even awful scenes, yet stand firm. One carer said, 'When I first began to take care of my father, he refused to have anyone come in to stay while I went out. He was pretty sick, so I didn't insist. Now, three years later, I haven't had a day away. He goes purple in the face at the very idea. I'm sure he'd have a heart attack if I went.'

Carers can be equally guilty of possessiveness. They can keep their parent to themselves with the result that a disabled parent is kept a virtual prisoner. One questions their motivations—are they afraid that someone else will rob them of the close relationship which has built up; or, if they know that they are a favoured beneficiary, that the parent may be persuaded to change the will; or because they feel powerful while controlling another's life?

It is not uncommon in a strict parent–child hierarchy for the parent quite bluntly to refuse to do what the daughter suggests, because she maintains that 'she will not be guided by her child'. Some elderly people can be steadfast in this attitude, and it can make the caring role very difficult. If your

52

mother reacts in this way, bring the GP, the health visitor or the social worker on to the scene. They will probably tell your mother a few home truths. The view of professional outsiders is generally acceptable and usually the old person will listen to them. It is sometimes necessary for an intermediary to interfere.

Of course, we must not overlook the possibility that disease will cause an old person's personality to change quite significantly. Gentle, kind parents can become insensitive and aggressive. If this happens to your mother, you may find that ultimately it seems impossible to have any respect or affection for her—the change may be so dramatic that she becomes no more than an externally familiar husk.

She may accuse you of robbing her, of physical abuse, of outrageous behaviour—it will pain you, but if you rely on your logic and assure yourself that the mother you once knew would be as appalled as you are at such behaviour, then perhaps you will be able to accept her behaviour more easily. If you decide to continue to care, bring in as many relief services as are available. Do not try to manage alone. Of course, it may be hard to find outsiders who will tolerate her attitude, but persevere.

On the other hand, if you find the situation too distressing, geriatric care may be the only answer. At the time, this may prove difficult and heart-rending, but in the long run it will most certainly be the best solution to the problem.

Other people's attitudes can produce anxiety and a sense of feeling despised in the elderly. For instance, we all know that some people, when speaking to an old, ill person, will tend to shout, and this can produce a feeling of inadequacy and distress in the old person.

There could be a tendency among some old people who are, in fact, capable of getting about, to take to their beds and, if they are not stirred, they will just fade away without trying to get going again. If your parent behaves in this fashion, ask her GP to come and give her a medical examination, or even to refer her to a psychiatrist to get her moving.

53

The caring role can have more severe problems than those which appear to the casual observer. It can happen for elderly (generally confused) parents to show some sexual aggression towards their carers, and this in turn can produce shame, apprehension and distress. If you find yourself in a situation of sexual advance, it is time you protected your own interests. Don't concern yourself about thwarting your parent's overtures; get a professional's advice.

As infirmity and disability increase, old people often become more and more anxious and depressed. We know that there are a number of reasons why depression is likely to occur in old age; retirement can curtail friendships among co-workers and produce a feeling of being useless and rejected by society; physical disability can limit activities outside the home and, equally soul-destroying, make it impossible to work on the house and garden; there will probably be reduced income which will seriously affect social activities. Death among former colleagues and family and friends, the feeling that one's own 'ticket' is coming up, incontinence, and increasing dependence on others, are some of the many factors which can contribute to depression. Physical debility or certain illnesses can create depression, too.

Your mother's depression can be one of the most difficult problems you have to face. The best treatment is your manifest love and affection. If she doesn't respond, can't sleep, loses interest in life generally, or becomes obsessed about any particular problem, then it's time to consult the GP. Some elderly people become so depressed that they contemplate suicide. It is not uncommon among older persons. A serious illness, the loss of a lifetime's partner, or just believing oneself to be a useless burden can lead an old person to contemplate this action. Don't believe the old myth that if people talk about suicide they won't carry it out. Where you suspect it is being considered, contact your mother's GP immediately.

Virtual isolation can adversely affect her. Just the two of

54

you being together can produce an artificial environment in which she becomes increasingly reliant on you until finally she reaches the stage where she vehemently resists any intervention from professionals or others. If she is capable of going out, encourage her to do so. A game of bridge once a week with a group in the next road, church, the weekly call to collect her pension—in other words, regular activity will tend to discourage her from becoming shut in.

Encourage her friends to ring, write or visit. One positive spin-off of her making frequent contact with them (which is often overlooked by the carer) is that she will feel safe in confiding her complaints about your attitudes and care, and in the long run this will rebound to your benefit in that she will probably be less liable to voice her discontent to you. If she has been severely ill and is now recuperating you may find that you have to accompany her several times on her initial outings to give her time to regain her confidence.

There is no doubt that where there is a good relationship, each of you will find deep satisfaction during this time. Your parent will feel secure and relaxed, being cared for in her own home, and you will feel happy that you have been able to give her such devoted attention. Yet even in the best relationship, you can become exhausted when greater demands are put on your time and energies, and therefore it is vital for you to protect yourself from the outset. Keep as much of your individuality as you can, and that means regularly getting away from caring, pursuing your own interests, and availing yourself of all available supportive services.

The constructive steps you can take are: to make sure that your parent's infirmity and/or disability has been thoroughly investigated so that you are certain that the treatment she is receiving is the appropriate one; ask the social worker or ring the home help organizer yourself and ask for a home help. If you cannot get one, and your mother has some capital, or if she receives the attendance allowance, pay for someone to come in to clean. If she needs to be bathed ask her GP to send in the district nurse.

A general word of caution here about your own attitude will not be out of place. Do not postpone calling in the available services because you believe you have all the answers. Your reluctance could culminate in your mental and/or physical collapse—there is a limit to what one person can cope with alone. A very intense caring pattern can build up, and you can become isolated, and as dependent on your role of carer as your parent is on you.

Your job can be helped greatly if she retains some of her independence as not only will you have to do less for her but, equally importantly, her morale will be higher.

Pay the neighbours or get a volunteer to come and stay with her if she cannot be left alone while you go out. It is critical to your whole relationship that each of you retains her individuality as far as possible.

It is necessary to be realistic about relationships and to acknowledge that not all relatives either like or admire one another. Some adult children make the unfortunate mistake of trying to gain affection they have never had, by returning home to take care of an infirm or disabled parent, and the result is often that the old person resents them even more, even despises them, and can show her reactions in quite unbelievable behaviour.

A number of middle-aged women 'baby' their mothers, and subconsciously try to satisfy the unfulfilled mother instinct through their parents. If this happens it can produce a premature dependency on the part of the old person and become a burden on the daughter herself.

The old person who has always been the dominant decision-maker will tend to treat the daughter as incapable of making them. It is important to resist this attitude from the very beginning, as if it persists you will undoubtedly become irritated, frustrated, and even angry.

Neither is it uncommon when one parent has died, for the remaining parent to put the adult child in the dead partner's place. Let us suppose that a father has died and an adult daughter is still at home, her mother can begin to rely on her

56

as she did the father even to the extent of calling her by the father's name. This complex situation will of course upset the daughter, and then at the time when the mother dies she will have to go through the trauma of re-establishing her role. If you see your mother slipping into such behaviour, tell her without anger that you are 'Jane' (or whoever) and you are not your father, and do not pander to her fantasies, as in the long run it would be more difficult for you both.

Frequently women complain that their years of care have impaired their mental and physical health. It appears that women generally begin caring between the ages of 35 and 52. In the majority of women, menopause begins somewhere in that age range. Today this physiological process can be devoid of discomfort and distress, yet many women do not ask their doctors for help. They let themselves become exhausted, they take no holiday and they still expect their bodies to function at maximum efficiency. Appreciating one's vulnerability is the first step. The next step is to protect oneself by getting in short- and long-term relief. We know that there are people who wallow in being the proverbial 'doormat', and regrettably nothing we can say will change their self-indulgent attitude.

At a highly personal emotional level, it is not unusual for some people who have not had a sexual relationship to feel frustrated, and for this gap in their lives to cause them distress and a sense of feeling rejected. For many this sexual frustration can lead to anger and bitterness, and being governed by a parent's priorities is no help.

Alternatively, because you have not had a relationship, you need not necessarily feel frustrated, as many people contentedly and avidly pursue work, hobbies, and sport to work off the surplus energy they would otherwise have invested in sexual activity. However, do not feel shy about discussing any disturbing awareness with your GP.

It is highly likely that, if the caring goes on, or if indeed it is intense, and particularly where you have night after night of broken sleep, that you will become thoroughly exhausted.

You may even reach the stage where every fibre and muscle in your body feels tired out and where you feel you cannot think straight. Some people turn to alcohol as an escape when they should be looking for relief from the burden. Remember that your parent's GP has the power to make arrangements (accommodation permitting of course) to have your mother admitted to a geriatric ward for a short time.

Full-time caring will generally mean that you will have to change your life-style. This may result in loss of contact with friends and less opportunity to take up leisure activities and interests, and having to live on a reduced income. Another source of frustration can be the realization that, although you have taken on the caring role, you are not in fact a born carer. Probably some element of frustration is healthy and can be released by physical or mental activity, such as taking the dog for a walk, digging in the garden, playing a piano, or painting. However, advanced degrees of frustration can be difficult to cope with if you are without help. If you feel at the end of your tether, get help from your doctor. Many exhausted, frustrated carers become impatient with the ill and elderly parents, and the constant strain of wear and tear can affect their mental as well as their physical stability. Having to cope with an old confused person constantly calling, with your own sleep being broken, with perpetually having to change your incontinent parent or just being together too much over a long period, can make you impatient, however normally equable your temper is, and if you do have an outburst you will generally feel guilty. You must have some help; ask your mother's GP to get a social worker to call so that you can talk over what is particularly aggravating you, or go to your own doctor, and explain and talk to him. Doctors are becoming more aware of the effects that the strain of long and intense care can have and are more willing to look for the root of your distress than to dismiss you with a packet of pills. Loss of patience can be an early indication that your own health is failing. Some people 'snap' under too much pressure; in extreme cases they can end up hurting

58

their parent, and then have to live with the added burden of guilt. Depending upon your ability to cope with strain, you may occasionally find that you are depressed. Depression can be attributable to a number of causes among which are the following: a dramatic reduction in your financial resources, your short- and long-term financial prospects being bleak; being effectively socially isolated with a feeling that there is no one in whom you can confide; your chances of a relation-ship with a member of the other sex being seriously reduced; your parent's increasing frailty with little or no chance of recovery; your physical exhaustion; lack of supportive ser-vices in your area; or your dependant's death. If you recog-nize that you are depressed, do not hesitate to seek medical help. Your GP may prescribe tranquillizers, he may relieve you of your parent's care by having her admitted to a geriatric unit for a period, or he may insist that you can no longer carry on and ask the social worker to arrange for your parent to be admitted to care.

Caring can produce an isolated situation for you. You can feel that no one else is interested in your predicament. You will undoubtedly feel isolated if you cannot go out and pur-sue your interests—it is amazing how many people get them-selves into the situation of not going out for a long period and then actually not wanting to go out. If you are on your own too much, for example, if your parent is senile, you may become introspective and end up by having a breakdown. Although you may not have been aware that your isolation was having an impact on your overall mental health, at the time when your parent does die, you could feel 'crippled' and be quite unable to cope. It is true that some people are more likely than others to get into an isolated con-dition—characteristically these are introspective, retiring, non-assertive people, who have probably always had a ten-dency to be that way inclined.

As the caring pattern is essentially set at its inception, the first few weeks of caring attitudes can be critical. Try to institute a flexible schedule so you can keep up your interests. Once a trend to isolation has commenced it can be broken only with difficulty, and many carers postpone stormy scenes because they feel either that their parents will 'win' in the end, or that they cannot put themselves through the additional tension and strain.

FIVE
Sources of Help

Professional, statutory, and voluntary

In an effort generally to alleviate your burden of caring I have briefly described the main functions of relevant professionals, and of statutory and voluntary bodies.

If you are embarking on the caring role, a knowledge of the available services should prove invaluable. There is a lot of evidence to suggest that many carers feel a hopelessness and helplessness with their circumstances and every carer, whether veteran or fledgeling, will benefit from supportive services.

If you can't cope, I have discussed some alternatives—sheltered housing, nursing homes and old people's homes.

Counsel and Care for the Elderly provides an advice and information service which should make it possible for you to contact the appropriate organizations needed to help you with your mother.

Do not be discouraged if the first person you contact is not the right one. Sometimes it will take you several letters or telephone calls, but ultimately you should be happy you persevered. The quality and quantity of services varies from region to region.

Remember that for some statutory services it is essential for you to have a recommendation from your mother's doctor or from the appropriate local welfare worker before you can claim such services.

Adaptations to the home

When your parent becomes disabled, she may find it easier to live on in her home if certain adaptations are made. The occupational therapist will advise on changes in the structure

61

or positioning of basic amenities, and financial assistance that can be obtained from the Social Services Department.

Among adaptations which may be helpful are: the installation of a stairlift; the installation of a ramp so that a wheelchair can be easily manoeuvred up and down; the installation of a downstairs toilet and bathroom (even though there may be one upstairs) and the conversion of a bathroom into a shower-room. Shower seats are very helpful to a disabled elderly person.

Day centres

Well-organized Day-care Centres perform three definite functions: they enable an old infirm person to be out among other people, 'My father is quite confused, but he still enjoys going out. He goes to a Day Centre three days a week, and I get some rest. I can cope, with that much help.' They give the carer a rest from what may otherwise be a perpetual routine of care, and they can enable a carer to go to work for at least part of the time.

Attendance at Day Centres varies; some people go daily, others attend for one or two days or for only a few hours a week. Arrangements to attend can be made through a social worker.

Transport, though it is sometimes poorly organized, is generally provided for those requiring it. Most Day-care Centres provide lunch.

Some Centres have programmes of occupational therapy, such as light industrial work, chair caning, printing, etc.

When the topic of going to a Day Centre is first broached, old people tend to resist the idea, but once their resistance is broken most people look forward to the change of routine and to the social contacts a trip to the Centre means.

Chiropody

Chiropody for elderly people is provided as part of the NHS through your local health authority. Special foot clinics are run by some health authorities and voluntary organizations. Consult your local health department or an old people's welfare organization (such as Age Concern) for a list of clinics in your neighbourhood (otherwise check in the Yellow Pages of the telephone directory).

When your mother first visits the chiropodist, advise her to take along her pension book, as a retirement pensioner can receive treatment free or at a reduced fee.

If your mother is unable to go to the chiropodist it may be possible to arrange a home visit.

District and Auxiliary nurses

The district nurse acts in the branches of home nursing which require a higher level of nursing knowledge than you are likely to have. She will give injections, treat gaping bed-sores and supervise medication. Your mother's GP may ask the nurse, who is variously known as a district nurse, domiciliary nurse, or home nurse, to call, or she can be telephoned at the health centre. The auxiliary nurse, who works under the district nurse's direction, gives general care, such as helping with dressing and undressing, washing, bathing etc. The district nurse can also advise you as to which medical supplies are free. If your parent is terminally ill, she will arrange for you to have a night sitter. If she is dying from cancer, the Marie Curie Fund can pay for a nurse to stay at night.

These professionals actually fulfil three functions: they perform the more skilled nursing functions, they give you confidence by advising what you should be doing, and they provide a regular social contact to break the isolation that can otherwise build up in a two-person household.

Equipment

Physical disability often means that aids and adaptations are necessary if any degree of independence is to be ensured. Your mother may be able to make use of one or more of the following aids. (These are normally provided free but some Social Services Departments do make a charge for them.)

For cooking and eating: a teapot stabilizer, a cooker guard, a wall can-opener, a grip to open stiff jars and bottles.

In the bedroom; a table which adjusts to fit over the bed, a special back rest or a bed which will adjust to a variety of different positions.

For the bathroom; a special tap attachment to facilitate turning on and off.

When getting dressed: gadgets for putting on stockings, and doing up zips.

In the sitting room: a comfortably adapted chair, a foot-stool and a leg rest.

For those with sight problems: a folding white stick, a braille alarm clock, braille playing cards, braille dominoes, a magnifying glass.

Aids for the deaf include a flashing light to alert a deaf person that a door bell has rung, and an amplifier for the telephone bell.

Aids to enable your mother to get about, such as a walking-stick, a frame, a ramp or crutches, can be borrowed from the physio-therapy department of her hospital. The nearest D.H.S.S. application centre will issue a wheelchair on recommendation.

Don't apply for (or buy) an aid unless the occupational therapist has assessed that it is needed.

As mentioned elsewhere in this book, Social Service Departments may carry out home adaptations such as the installation of a ramp, handrails, etc. to give your mother greater mobility.

For more information on aids, contact the Disabled Living Foundation. (See Chapter Ten).

The General Practitioner

Nowadays it is almost impossible to have as the family doctor the doctor who brought you into the world and who has seen and listened to all the family's physical and emotional ups and downs. The GP is still, however, one of the most valuable professionals involved in the relationship between carer and dependant. At practical level, he can set the existing supportive services system into motion.

Where an old person's health is concerned, the carer must be the 'watch-dog' for any new symptoms or changes. If the doctor is consulted, he should be informed of any changes at all that have been noted. A symptom that may appear unimportant to a carer may in fact be of great value to the GP in making his diagnosis.

If the GP advises a hospital admission, he should be given every co-operation from the carer. He is the professional and has good reason for his advice.

At times you will be worn out yourself, and should explain your weariness to your own doctor. A concerned doctor will intervene here to see that you get some respite. Long-term caring may produce acute or chronic depression and/or anxiety, and the doctor should be able to help you over these low periods. He may advise short-term care for your parent, while you have a rest, or longer term, in which your parent should be admitted to full-time residential care.

It is important not to be talked into the way of thinking that just because a dependant is, say 89, not much else can be expected of her health.

If you are dissatisfied with your parent's doctor's attitude, or the care she is receiving from him, it is possible to make a formal complaint to the Family Practitioner Committee.[1] However, in all fairness, the cause of discontent should be discussed with the GP first. But if no satisfaction is forthcoming, the GP should be changed.

Keep the doctor's telephone number beside the telephone for use in an emergency.

[1] In Scotland, complaints against a GP must be made in writing to the Secretary of the Health Board within six weeks of the cause of the complaint.

Geriatric Day-hospitals

One source of support is the geriatric day-hospital. These are usually in general hospital grounds, and patients can go to them on one or more days a week for occupational therapy or physio-therapy. This scheme enables an old person to remain at home in cases where, otherwise, permanent residence in hospital might be necessary. Arrangements to attend such a hospital can be made by your mother's GP.

Health Visitors

Health visitors are fully qualified nurses, who have gone through extra training. Most health visitors belong to what is known as a Primary Health Team.

The health visitor does not actually do any nursing. That work is left to the district nurse. A health visitor is trained to relieve anxieties and tensions that build up in a caring household; she should recognize any early signs of illness, and she knows the details of the services available—social, housing, and voluntary services.

You may ask your mother's GP to arrange for the health visitor to call, or you can ask for the help of a health visitor direct, by phoning the doctor's surgery.

Generally, the health visitor will prove increasingly valuable as your mother's demands on you increase.

Transport to a Hospital Out-patients' Clinic

If your mother's income is below a certain limit, and she is sent by her GP to an out-patients' clinic, she can claim a refund on fares for public transport to and from hospital. If she is too ill to cope with public transport, ask the doctor to arrange for an ambulance or hospital car to take her there. As already mentioned, this transport can be rather poorly organized, and your mother may find that, after she has seen the doctor, occupational therapist, etc., she is sitting in a chair against a wall with a lot of other elderly sick persons for several hours, waiting to be driven home. You can alleviate the strain of the wait by sending along a flask of tea and some biscuits, her knitting, or a book. Apart from getting stiff and very tired, waiting can be quite depressing, especially if she is sitting by Mrs T. who insists on telling her the last gory detail of her 'awful stomach op'! When she gets home, she'll probably be a bit 'scratchy' and ready for bed.

It would be remiss of me to make the acquisition of social services appear simple, when in fact, you may find the whole process frustrating and tiresome. If all the services available were always in proper and efficient communication, your role would be devoid of many problems; however, personnel are often overworked and departments under-staffed. Appreciating this state of affairs, do not give in, keep up your efforts to obtain the social services to which you believe you are entitled.

Home Amenities

Although having a hand-basin, lavatory, etc. installed may cause temporary dislocation in the household, it should prove of benefit to your caring demands in the long run. Don't take the attitude that it isn't worth it, as your mother may live only another two months; old people do survive serious illnesses and two months could extend to twenty years!

On the other hand, if the whole idea distresses her, don't be adamant that your mother, who is still coping well and who has washed in a bowl all her married life, must have a bathroom installed for her benefit. If she is happy with a bowl and she wants to continue to live that way, leave her as she is. Many of us try to impose our 'new-fangled' standards on our parents, and cause them more anxiety than pleasure.

Housing Grants

Before an intermediate grant for installation of 'standard' amenities, such as a bath, hot and cold water, or an indoor

WC, or grants for replacements and repairs necessary to bring the house up to a fair state of repair can be given, the following conditions must be satisfied:

The house must be freehold owned, or leased (with at least five years to run) and be lived in or rented out by the applicant; and have been without one or more of the standard amenities for at least a year.

The work must not begin before the grant is approved, and must be finished by the date the council sets.

After the work has been done, the house must be in a good state of repair, and so be fit to live in for at least another fifteen years, and there must not be any plans to demolish it in that period. Another requirement is that the house must comply with the Building Regulations for roof insulation.

To apply for a grant, contact one of the Improvement Grants Officers in the City Engineer's Department, or one of the Housing Officers in the Chief Environmental Health Officer's Department. He will usually arrange for someone to visit you to discuss whether grants are available for the works you want done.

After the officer's advisory visit, you must obtain an estimate and have a plan prepared. When you have these you can put in an application.

If the complete application is accepted, the Council will arrange to inspect the premises concerned, to determine the eligible expense of the grant-aided work. The next step will be for you to satisfy the City Solicitor as to your legal title to the property.

Ultimately, you will be informed of the eligible cost of the improvements approved by the Council, and the amount of the grant.

Where the house is occupied by a disabled person, an intermediate grant can be made for an alternative standard amenity if an existing one is inaccessible to him or her.

Except in special areas, a grant will be made for half of the cost up to a specified level of each amenity that has to be put in.

Housing Departments are required to consider the needs of disabled people in new housing schemes. Two of the types of housing that could help your caring are:

Wheelchair housing, which is designed to give people in wheelchairs access to all principal rooms, including bathrooms and lavatories;

Mobility housing, which is designed for less severely disabled people.

In these schemes the entrances are level or ramped, and the entrance corridors and doors of principal rooms, though not bathroom or lavatory, are wide enough for a normal wheelchair. The bathroom, lavatory and at least one bedroom are on the same level as the entrances. Such housing could lighten your caring burden considerably and should not be overlooked.

Home Helps

One of the most important supportive people you can have when you are caring for an elderly ill person is a home help. One carer said:

The Home Help is a treasure. She has 'adopted' us. She cashes mother's pension, does the shopping, brings her a piece of cake or pie from home, stays longer than she is obliged to, does a good two hours' work whenever she comes, and helps prevent my mother from being so lonely.

Many home helps build up a very special type of relationship with their clients; they can assume the role of a friend to many elderly and relatively isolated people. As far as you are concerned, their presence can be a safety valve. Relieving you of the burden of some of the housework is important but, additionally, having someone to talk to about your problems, on a very casual basis, can be just as important.

You can apply direct to the Social Services Department for a home help. When you apply, don't hesitate to tell them just how overburdened you are. Some Social Services Departments will not make a home help available where there is a single woman in the household.

If the presence of a home help on one or two mornings a week will enable you to keep your job, it is essential for you to acquire one, even if you have to pay for her services yourself.

If you are working full or part time, a home help fulfils several roles: she does the housekeeping essentials; she alleviates your mother's isolation while you are away, she builds up a relationship with your mother which precludes you from being the only person in your mother's life, and additionally, she can keep an eye on her and will generally notice any change in her overall health.

If your mother objects to having a home help, perhaps the home help organizer or social worker can talk to her and explain the advantages, particularly stressing the alleviation of part of your overall burden.

If a home help is made available, your mother's financial position will be assessed to determine whether or not she should pay anything towards the service. If she receives supplementary benefit she will be provided with the home help free of charge. The better off your mother is the more she will be required to pay—which is fair enough.

In the event of your mother's being admitted to hospital, inform the home help organizer immediately. If you have a complaint to make, speak or write to the home help organizer.

Intermittent Admissions

If your mother is senile or incontinent, or if you have actually reached the stage where you feel you can no longer cope, you can ask her GP to arrange for her to be admitted to short-term care, so that you can have a complete rest.

From a longer-term point of view, if you believe that, with some regular relief, you can carry on, ask your mother's GP to inquire into the possibility of your mother's being admitted for alternate weeks or every two weeks for this type of care.

Meals on Wheels

This service can satisfy various needs. If your mother is generally infirm and has few outside contacts, yet is still able to cope, meals on wheels can do two things: they can bring another contact on to the scene, and they can provide her with a hot lunch. (Reports on the quality of the cooking vary!)

If you are still working, the meals on wheels service will help you to avoid a frantic rush home in order to provide your mother with both a meal and company.

The social worker can arrange for this service.

The W.R.V.S (the helpful ladies in green uniform) is generally the organization responsible for delivering the meals on wheels. A minimal charge is made for each meal, but note that it would generally cost as much to provide the meal yourself.

Occupational Therapists

The main task of the occupational therapist is to teach newly disabled individuals how to adapt to reduced capabilities in an unchanged environment, and this includes learning new ways of doing commonplace things, such as dressing and undressing, eating, and housework. In doing so, the therapist will lay great stress on making the parent believe and see that she can still be useful and take care of these aspects of living herself, as this attitude is of great importance for the mental health and happiness of an old person.

71

The majority of occupational therapists (or O.T.s) work in hospitals and are linked with consultants in many fields apart from geriatric medicine. It is not unusual for them to ask to see the carer, so as to show her how she can help the old person to adapt and become independent. If she fails to do this, and there is cause to worry as the old person's ability to care for herself is significantly reduced, it is wise to ask the sister-in-charge to arrange a meeting so as to discuss these matters.

Hospital-based O.T.s often pay home visits before the old person is discharged from hospital. She may make this visit in the company of the old person or she may meet the carer in the old person's home. The purpose of the visit is to discuss any alterations or adaptations she may think necessary.

The domiciliary O.T. who is based in the community and has had exactly the same training as the hospital O.T., takes over when the old person is discharged from hospital. She can be contacted direct. For information as to how to do so, contact the old person's health visitor or the Social Services Department in the area in which the old person lives. The O.T. can advise on ways to make the old person less dependent.

One of the most difficult things you may have to do is to avoid giving assistance to someone elderly, who may be distressed and struggling feebly to perform some task. This difficulty may be heightened by well-meaning onlookers who do not always realize that it is to her long-term advantage if she succeeds in overcoming her own handicaps. For she knows what she could once do and she will never really be happy until she can feel that she can do it again, or that she will do so in the future.

The O.T. is the ideal person with whom to discuss these problems. She is experienced in helping disabled people and in dealing with the emotions that the disablement induces in the disabled and in their supporters.

Physio-therapists

There are domiciliary physio-therapists in some places; these professionals are generally allocated by the GP or sent by the hospital to give the follow-up treatment. Generally, however, the GP will refer a patient to the hospital for treatment.

If a physio-therapist's treatment is to have its full impact the patient must co-operate with her. Among those people whom the physio-therapist helps greatly are most stroke patients, arthritics, and people who have had an accident. If your parent is referred to a physio-therapist, encourage her to undergo the recommended treatment.

Short-term care

As far as possible, look at your caring role as a definite job. Employees have holidays; in their absence, the office or the industry survives! Don't lead yourself to believe that you are indispensable. The geriatric ward, the nursing home or cousin Emma, will cope in your absence.

Although your dependant may aggressively resist any change of carer, you must insist that you have to have a rest. Ironically enough the old person usually benefits as much from the change of scene as the carer. From the very outset organize as many breaks as practicable. It is fatal to keep on postponing the decision to take a rest.

Where your mother is to be admitted to a short-stay geriatric ward, or a short-stay nursing home, go along with her while she settles in. Do not thoughtlessly just 'dump' her, as this could make her feel unwanted, neglected and apprehensive. Be positive about the temporary environment; become acquainted with the routine, introduce yourself to the staff, inform them of any 'quirks' your mother may have and ask whether an extra blanket, Coffee-Mate in coffee, apple-blossom talcum powder, or whatever her fancies are, are permitted. Often it is the small things that either make or break when settling into a new environment.

Social Services Departments

The Social Services Department performs the job of the grandmothers, aunts, and neighbours in earlier times. They assist you to get the most appropriate help that is available for your particular case, and should not be rejected or resented merely because they are seen as 'outsiders'. You would have been inclined to accept your aunt's advising, 'Don't you think it would be better if your mother slept downstairs, nearer the lavatory? I moved Tom when he was ill and it saved my life.' When the social worker, who is a total stranger, twenty-three, and businesslike, comes in and suggests the same you may be inclined to be resentful. Also you may be embarrassed about your dilapidated furnishings. However, may I remind you that the whole fabric of society has changed in your lifetime, and although you may not like young social workers coming in, you no longer have a close network of family, or local sages, to fall back on for basic advice and strength. Therefore, close your eyes to the raggy sheets, to the holes in the kitchen curtains, etc. (which others rarely notice as much as we notice ourselves!), and do the sensible thing and get the help of the Social Services Department staff. If what you basically need are the support services, then the Department of Social Services is the body that can provide them.

The Social Services Department of the local authority department (The Social Works Department in Scotland) responds to the problems of the aged under three headings: information, supportive services and residential accommodation.

As regards the first of these, they supply detailed information on their own services, and other services relating to housing, legal aid and finance.

The supportive services that the Department supplies for the elderly are home helps, meals on wheels, Day Centres, and transport to and from them, home improvements, telephones, lunch clubs and a laundry service in the case of incontinence.

However, services vary from area to area, so be prepared for differences in supply and quality.

The Department also provides residential accommodation and supervises the operation of voluntary homes for old people.

Social Workers

The Department will provide the services of a social worker. These professionals are trained to improve the situation in which an old person lives. She will make decisions as to which domiciliary services an old person should receive, and whether or not she should go into residential care.

If you feel that you need a social worker to advise you about your elderly mother, write to the local Social Services department, describing your difficulties. The social worker will get in touch with you after about a week.

In an emergency, you can phone the Department or go there. After normal office hours, you should ring an emergency number. This number can be obtained by ringing the number listed for the Social Services Department in the telephone directory.

Telephones

Under certain circumstances the local authority may consider the installation of a telephone for your mother. If she lives alone, or is frequently alone, or receives the attendance allowance and has a medical condition which may require urgent contact with a doctor, auxiliary medical officer or helper, and is in danger or at risk unless she has a telephone, one will undoubtedly be provided.

Other cases in which a telephone may be provided are where she is a registered blind person, or she is unable to leave the house in normal weather without the help of someone else and so may become isolated.

Relief sitters-in

It is absolutely vital for you to get a break away from caring. You should try to see that you get short-term and long-term rest.

Short-term rest can mean a walk round the block every day without fail (at least), and a sitter-in to relieve you as often as can be arranged. If you make use of outside resources, a Day Centre or a short-day geriatric unit can temporarily take the burden off you.

It is common for many old people to refuse to accept a substitute carer, even for short periods.

Generally our whole social structure conditions us to expect that the only acquaintances for whom we can expect to develop any trust, liking or feeling are those we seek out. This attitude can affect our reactions to those who are essentially thrust in our paths. In addition to this feeling the elderly see the sitter-in as someone who, to all intents and purposes, will have an element of 'official authority' over them.

At the beginning the right attitude on your part can often prevent stubborn resistance to a relief sitter-in later on. It is quite useless for me to direct any advice towards veteran carers, because in all probability a pattern of behaviour has been established, and it would take heaven and earth to change it.

For those of you who anticipate becoming carers, or for those of you who have more recently assumed the caring role, I cannot over-emphasize that you must be firm about having time off.

One of the tactics some old people use to try to ensure that their carers don't leave them, is to plead that they will die if someone else comes in as carer, or if they are left on their own; even for a brief period. You yourself, when you were young, probably reacted in a similar vein if your mother wanted to leave you, and you used stomach pains, sore throat, ear-ache, etc. as 'weaponry'.

Don't be angry, don't make a fuss, but do be firm. Arguing

is generally a useless waste of time and energy. Make your plans, explain them, and then adhere to them.

It is unrealistic to imagine that every volunteer brought in as a relief sitter-in will either be accepted, or indeed, will want to stay. Arrange that whoever it is that is expected visits at least once with you there. You must be aware that just because someone is being kind hearted, it does not necessarily mean they are sensible, agreeable people.

If you are paying the sitter-in, it is equally important for contact to be made before she actually undertakes the responsibility.

Where a potential sitter-in appears to be acceptable, try to discuss what her interests are; the sojourn could be more pleasant for your mother and the sitter for example, if they play two-handed whist, cribbage, draughts, read poetry, discuss pickle-making, or whatever.

A successful relief sitter-in set-up can have several benefits. Both you and your mother will be spared the monotony of each other's constant company; your mother will retain her 'social skills' and confidence longer, you will get away from the caring scene and won't feel guilty about leaving, and the overall caring burden should be reduced.

Finding sitters-in may prove difficult. The aspects you have to consider are what you expect her to do, and whether or not you want to pay her and, if you do pay, from whose income she should be paid. Use your mother's income to pay relief sitters-in before you use your own. Many carers use the non-means-tested Attendance Allowance for this purpose.

For longer-term relief, the National Council for the Single Woman and Her Dependants has a list of women who will go into homes to care for an elderly person while the daughter or caring family member takes a holiday.

For paid sitters-in, pay your neighbour to come in, or get a private nurse.

For volunteers, approach Age Concern's local organizing secretary, your church's Women's Guild, or contact your local WRVS or British Red Cross.

Private nursing

You can hire a qualified nurse from a nursing agency, a list of which can be found in the telephone directory. You should note that their services (added to which is the agency fee) are expensive. It is advisable to check on exactly how much an hour a private nurse's fee will be before you arrange to bring one into the house.

SIX
Finance

As financial benefits are subject to periodic change, you should check at least every 6 months that the amount you are receiving is the correct one and that you don't qualify for some recently introduced payments.

I have organized the information about financial benefits into two categories to make it easier for you to find the important points on the benefits which should be most relevant to your situation as a carer. Summaries of the Attendance Allowance (your parent's benefit); the Invalid Care Allowance, and the Supplementary Benefit are in this first section, and details of these benefits and the other benefits (which will be referred to less frequently) are in the appendix.

Financial benefits in caring

The financial benefit which your parent may claim is the Attendance Allowance; and you may claim the Invalid Care Allowance and Supplementary Benefit.

I have briefly outlined claim conditions here but you can find more information on these benefits in the appendix.

Your parent may claim the Attendance Allowance (tax free, without being means tested, and in addition to any other income or benefits she receives) provided she needs either frequent attention throughout the day in connection with her bodily functions or constant supervision to prevent danger to herself or others, or prolonged or repeated attention during the night in connection with her bodily functions or continued supervision throughout the night to avoid substantial danger to herself and others. There are two rates; the higher rate is applicable if she needs attention both by day *and* night. It is not necessary for anyone in the household to give up work before the Attendance Allowance can be claimed and some families have used the extra income to pay for help in the home so that the wage-earner can continue in employment. If your elder is refused the Attendance Allowance, she should keep on trying to obtain it, as it has been shown that many once-turned-down claimants succeed at the second or even subsequent attempts.

If she receives the Attendance Allowance, and you have given up your work to care for her, and you are under pensionable age, you may be able to obtain the Invalid Care Allowance. This benefit is paid without test of means (but is taxable if there is tax liability) and carries with it a Class 1 contribution credit for your national insurance record. Depending on your financial circumstances you may also be eligible for a Supplementary Benefit allowance.

If you receive the Invalid Care Allowance you can earn up to £6 net weekly without losing your entitlement to benefit. You can deduct certain expenses from the gross—fares to work, tools and equipment, excessive wear and tear of normal clothing, the cost of any meal taken during working hours up to 15p (provided your employer does not issue luncheon vouchers) and the cost of providing for the necessary care of a member of the household during your absence at work (write to the Social Security office for the full list of deductible expenses).

Your State pension rights, if you have given up work for home caring, may be protected by the Home Responsibilities Protection regulations which came into effect in April 1978 as part of the new pensions legislation.

You should of course check that your mother is receiving all the benefits and allowances to which she is entitled.

Further details about current amounts, scope and conditions of the forementioned benefits are contained in the Financial Benefits Appendix (see p. 142).

Finance generally

Good monetary planning will make you look at the financial side of your life from both short- and long-term aspects. If you are still working, you should ask yourself what are your future job goals, salary levels and family circumstances. Is there a real possibility that you may have to relinquish your main source of income, your salary, because you will be caring full time?

Some knowledge of budgeting, investing, annuities, insurance, capital transfer tax, and tax generally is essential, if you are to be able to take constructive measures to protect yourself from financial anxiety. The following sections are intended only as introductions to their subjects. (See *Lady, Watch your Money* by H. McKenzie, published by John Clare Books for more details in any one area.)

Your bank manager will be only too happy to advise you on investing. The Inland Revenue officer will advise you on your tax problems.

Budgeting

Regardless of your income you will have a tendency to live up to it, therefore it is very sensible to set yourself a budget. This is essential for those with a very low income if they are not to get into severe difficulty. Don't assume responsibility for all the expenditure, while your parent puts her income away for the family! Make two tables; set down (a) the sources of income coming into the house, and (b) the entire outgoings for the year. (See table).

Make sure that all the benefits to which your dependant and you are entitled are being claimed. When you have your total divide it by 52 to get your weekly financial position.

Some simple tips are: As a rule of thumb shop no more than twice a week if you possibly can. Make out a list and stick to it. The exception to this rule is to buy as much bulk dry goods and tinned goods as you can afford and store.

81

SOURCES OF INCOME

For your mother:
> Retirement Pension
> Attendance Allowance
> Annuities
> Dividends

For yourself:
> Invalid Care Allowance
> Supplementary Benefit or Salary

Total=£

OVERALL OUTGOINGS

Standing
Group A:
necessary and	Rent or Mortgage
not subject to	Household Maintenance
much change	Taxation (see end
	of chapter)

Household
Group B:
necessary but	Fuel
more variable	Food
than Group A	Telephone
	Clothes
	Chemist Bills

Extras
Group C:
Can generally be	Transport
tailored to fit	Dentist
the budget	Holidays
	Entertainment etc.

Total = £

Don't let your kitchen cupboard space determine how much bulk you should buy in if you have convertible space in other rooms—for instance an unused wardrobe is a first-rate storage cupboard for tinned goods. If you have some land, grow vegetables.

Some useful hints on making things go further are: Cook vegetables in a covered pan in a minimum of lightly salted boiling water to preserve nourishment and fuel; if you boil a kettle of water, make up the left-over water into a thermos of tea; use old bread up by encrumbling it for meat loaves, toppings, etc.—all you do is put it into the oven until it is crisp; use powdered milk instead of fresh milk where you can; put a sugar lump in the biscuit tin to keep the biscuits crisp; rinse an 'empty' detergent bottle with water to get an extra lot of suds.

Buy clothes for next year; a sale item may need a few stitches in it, but don't let that deter you from buying an otherwise good-quality garment. A bit of velvet sewn on a collar and cuffs will give an old dress a new look. It is often possible to pick up little-worn garments at a jumble sale and in some cases to turn them and make another garment out of them. For instance, you may get a waistcoat out of a jacket, etc. If you have good eyesight and non-arthritic hands you can sew—if you don't, you are really being lazy.

Paying bills

Everyone has bills to pay and for someone pre-occupied at home, this can be a chore. Any one of the following may therefore help you:

STANDING ORDERS

These are useful for regular payments in set amounts, such as, insurance premiums, etc. Tell the bank, through instructions on a printed form, to pay the amount when it comes due.

BANK GIRO

Saves postage. Once the bank has the giro slip it will make the transfers, stamping the bill as evidence of payment.

DIRECT DEBIT

You instruct your creditors (people to whom you owe the money) to claim it from your bank and you instruct the bank to accept such claims and to debit your account.

BUDGET ACCOUNTS

Many large department stores run a budget account system of one sort or another. The banks provide a similar service. In these you estimate all your expected outgoings for the year, adding on a percentage for inflation, and divide the total by 12 which gives the monthly amount to go from your current account into your budget account to pay your bills.

Are you sure you are getting the maximum income out of your investments? Do you want immediate income or are you more interested in longer-term investing?

Stocks and shares

If you invest on the stock market you should consult a broker who will have to be paid a commission on the transactions involved. Gains can be made but losses can equally be incurred, therefore it is wise not to put all your 'eggs into one basket'.

DIVIDENDS

Tax deductions are generally made before dividends are paid on stocks and shares.

Government securities

A government security is a promise by the Government to repay, normally at a specified future date, money borrowed in the past, and in the interval, to pay the owner interest at a stated rate.

The advantages of investment in these securities is that they pay higher rates of interest than are obtainable in most other ways. If purchased through a bank or broker they can be sold immediately by contacting the broker. One possible disadvantage of government security investment is that as their value is not actually fixed, you can lose money if their value declines; however, you can on the other hand, make money if their value rises. Most government securities are also obtainable through the post office.

There are four categories of Government stock: (a) Short-dated (repaid at face value within five years). These can have a lower rate of interest but give a capital gain; (b) Medium-dated. These are repayable between five and fifteen years; (c) Long-dated, repayable after fifteen years; (d) Undated. These are speculative and should be bought only if you have had expert advice. There is no tax on capital gains for government securities held for more than one year.

Retirement annuity policies

Premiums on these policies are allowable for tax relief and the funds in which they are invested are tax exempt. At retirement you do not have to take out the entire sum all at once; instead, you get an income for the rest of your life. Some of this income is regarded as capital repayment and is free of tax.

Unit Trusts

In these trusts investors pool their resources into a profes-sionally managed fund. The fund is divided into equal units which belong to the holders in proportion to the amount they have put into it.

If you are thinking about investing in a unit trust do so

when the market is low. Income tax standard-rate deductions are generally made before dividends are paid on unit trusts.

Equity Bonds

The value of these bonds, which can fluctuate widely, is directly related to funds of stocks and shares which are managed either by an insurance company or other professional managers. Generally equity bonds can be switched into managed or property bonds at any time for only a nominal charge.

Property Bonds

Through these bonds money is invested in funds comprising freeholds or leaseholds, industrial or commercial property. Valuations can vary widely; you should know a great deal about property values before you venture into this type of portfolio.

Banks

Check that the bank in which you have your money pays the highest rate of interest on savings accounts.

Private Banks

These generally offer a high rate of interest. Check out the firm's reputation before you invest in private bank deposits.

Loans to Local Authorities

These offer a safe investment for a limited period at a rate of interest somewhat higher than those offered by government securities. Presently the rates offered are between 13% and 16% for various sums of £100 plus for differing periods, generally between one to ten years (some offer longer terms). Watch for advertisements on these loans in the financial pages of the daily or Sunday papers. You can also get information on what is being offered from the Chartered Institute of Public Finance and Accountancy, 232 Vauxhall Bridge Road, London SW1.

Annuities

The principle behind annuity buying is that by paying a lump sum to an insurance company you will get a guaranteed income for life. Only part of your annuity payments are liable to tax, the part regarded as investment income. The amount of tax depends on the age of the purchaser at the time the annuity was bought. The disadvantages are that the capital will be beyond your control and the value will be eroded by inflation.

Ask any investment broker or insurance broker which annuity would be best for you.

Mortgage Annuities

If either you or your parent has a reasonably high income but little capital, and this is tied up in the home you/she may possibly benefit from a mortgage annuity. Under this scheme, if either of you is over 68 years of age a mortgage against up to 75 per cent of the value of the house can be taken out. The loan is invested in an annuity which will provide a fixed income for the rest of one's life. At death, the loan is repaid out of the estate. Your mother may be able to pay for more supportive help through such a scheme. However, any interest in the house you had expected to devolve upon you at her death will accordingly be affected, because the house will have to be sold at your parent's death.

National Savings Certificates

The current issue is the 19th. The maximum amount that anyone can buy in this series is £1500 worth. This amount is not affected by holdings in other series.

Each certificate costs £10 and matures after five years when it then has a value of £16.35. Earlier encashment gives a smaller return. Any gain is free of all tax.

The rate in interest increases over the life of the certificate. this is illustrated in the table given below:

END OF YEAR	VALUE	TAX FREE YIELD FOR YEAR
1	£10.50	5 per cent
2	£11.25	8.57 per cent
3	£12.24	9.21 per cent
4	£13.50	13.25 per cent
5	£15.00	15.96 per cent

For the whole five years the yield is equivalent to 10.33 per cent compound interest.

Certificates may be bought from most post offices and banks. They may be sold only to the Department of National Savings. To sell, holders have to apply to the Director, Savings Certificates and SAYE Office, Durham DH99 1NS. The necessary application forms and franked envelopes, fully addressed, may be obtained at most post offices. Eight clear working days' notice are required to complete the sale.

RETIREMENT ISSUE—INDEX-LINKED

Men of 65, women of 60 can buy these and one need not have retired. They come in £10 units with the maximum holding £1200 for each person. In addition to the 4% interest paid at the end of five years, the increase in value is based on the difference between the Retail Price Index (R.P.I.) in the month of purchase and the R.P.I. in the month of withdrawal.

The R.P.I. figures for each month are on display in the Post Office.

Building Societies

Building societies offer various types of accounts:

SHARE ACCOUNT

Many people use this account. Interest rates are now around 10.5 per cent. You don't have to agree to pay in any fixed amount. Either you can leave the interest in your account or you can have it sent to you twice a year. A third way is to have it paid into a bank account. Note that most societies, certainly the larger ones, offer a higher rate of interest if the investor is prepared to give three months' or six months' withdrawal notice.

MONTHLY INTEREST ACCOUNTS

Some societies agree to pay interest monthly.

SAVE AS YOU EARN (S.A.Y.E.)

If you are willing and able to make monthly savings of fixed amounts for five years, you will get a tax-free bonus equal to 14 monthly savings. If you leave the whole sum where it is for a further two years your tax-free bonus will be doubled. (See also below for SAYE by the Post Office index-linked scheme.)

TERM SHARES

Ask at your Building Society about these.

INCOME TAX ON BUILDING SOCIETY INTEREST

Building Societies pay interest on the basis that the standard rate of tax has been deducted. If you are liable to a reduced or a nil rate of tax, this, in contradistinction to most other forms of tax, cannot be reclaimed. It is therefore inadvisable for people paying less than the current standard rate of tax (and particularly those not liable at all for tax) to place their money in building society accounts. Savings Bank (*q.v*) or National Savings Certificates (*q.v.*) are a better bet.

89

The Post Office Savings Account

Having a Post Office Savings Account is very popular. Small sums can be deposited and withdrawals of up to £50 can be made at one time. If you want to withdraw more than £50 you must make special application on a form which can be obtained from the Post Office. Interest is paid at the rate of 5 per cent per annum (current rate). The first £70 of this interest is tax free. In choosing this investment one has to balance the relative merits of £70 free of tax and the low rate of interest.

Save As You Earn (S.A.Y.E.)

The current issue of S.A.Y.E. is 'index-linked'—i.e. linked to the rate of inflation. The saver agrees to make monthly payments of from £4 to £20 (this applies to people over 16 years of age) for five years—totalling 60 payments. At the end of this time repayment is made including an adjustment made to compensate for the ravages of inflation. Payments may be made by a Standing Order on your bank or by National Giro Account or by cash at a post office. Some employers use a National Savings Bank Transfer Account in order to allow monthly contributions to be made direct to the S.A.Y.E. office by automatic deductions from weekly or monthly pay.

With inflation at its present rate this provides a return on your money as high as any obtainable although, of course, no interest, as such, is earned during the five year period. Other savings schemes, it should be realized, pay interest rates which look better but which are, in fact, negative as the percentage of interest is less than the percentage of inflation. Similarly with non-index-linked schemes, if you withdraw, say, £100 invested six months ago, its purchasing power will assuredly have dropped in the meantime.

In the event that payments are discontinued after 12 but before 60 have been made, the contributions will be returned without index-linking, but with tax-free interest at 6 per cent per annum. In the first year the contributions are merely returned.

After completion of sixty payments the money may be left for further indexing for another two years. At this stage, seven years after starting, a tax-free bonus equal to two months' contributions is received. This bonus corresponds to simple interest of about 1 per cent per annum on the sums invested. It is rather insignificant in comparison with the effect of inflation but it does correspond to a real gain.

The least amount returned is guaranteed to equal the payments. There is therefore no danger of loss due to an unlooked-for drop in the Retail Price Index (R.P.I.).

(See also S.A.Y.E under Building Societies).

Income from letting part of one's home

You or your mother will not have to pay income tax on the value of the house owned and lived in. If, however, part of it is let (whether or not it is let furnished or unfurnished) the income received from the letting has to be included in your/her tax returns.

Capital Transfer Tax

Capital Transfer Tax is applied to gifts made during a person's lifetime as well as to possessions at death. The answer to the question of what can count as a taxable gift, if given away, is everything. At the time when a deceased person's estate is distributed that distribution is interpreted as giving away everything he or she owned.

There are certain gifts that are tax free but after these are excluded any other gift counts as a taxable gift. The basic rule to know about Capital Transfer Tax is that there is no tax on the first £25 000 of gifts. The next principle is that everyone has one running total which covers gifts made in life and death. Remember, therefore, that on someone's death any remaining possessions are added to his or her running total.

A husband and wife have their own individual running totals. Each can make his/her own tax-free gifts, and can each make £25 000 of taxable gifts before having to pay any Capital Transfer Tax.

Tax-free gifts covered are those which are tax free whenever they are made and those which are tax free only when made in life. Tax-free gifts in life and on death include those between husband and wife, the first £100 000 of gifts to charities, and gifts to national institutions.

Gifts tax free only on death are lump sums paid to one's dependants(s) from an employment pension scheme and reasonable funeral expenses.

Gifts tax free only in life are gifts made out of income which are part of normal spending, gifts of up to £100 each to any number of different people, gifts to support a person's or his wife's elderly (65 or over) or infirm relatives or to support a widowed, separated, or divorced mother or mother-in-law, gifts to maintain an ex-husband or wife, wedding gifts up to £500, where one is parent of a bride or groom, or £2500 if one is a grandparent or great-grandparent, up to £2000 worth of gifts during any tax year which don't count as tax free for any other reason.

Some ways of saving Capital Transfer Tax are: keeping a running total of taxable gifts made so you will know in advance what has to be paid on any new gift; using every opportunity of making tax-free gifts (such as a £100 gift); a husband and wife dividing their possessions between them; parents leaving their possessions to their children instead of to each other; making sure a will is set out to save estate duty; taking out a life insurance policy in favour of one's children.

From the above you will recognize that your parent can probably save Capital Transfer Tax.

Age Allowance

Taxpayers who are aged 65 during 1979–80 receive special age allowance of £1540. This is increased to £2455 for a married couple if either the husband or wife is 65 or over at any time during the year ended on 5 April 1980.

The age allowance is in substitution for, and not in addition to, the single or married personal allowance which is given at reduced levels. If total income exceeds £5,000 the age allowance will be reduced by £2 for each £3 income of income over £5,000. This keeps up until the age allowance is reduced to the single personal allowance of £1165, or the married allowance of £1815 at which time the age allowance will not apply and only the normal single or married personal allowance may be obtained.

Personal Allowance

A lower personal allowance of £1165 is allowed for single people and widows and widowers below the age of 65.

Housekeeper Allowance

An allowance of £100 is available to a widower if a relative (whether male or female) resides with him to act as housekeeper.

Son or daughter's services allowance

An allowance of £55 may be claimed where by reason of her age or infirmity a taxpayer has to depend on the services of a son or daughter resident with and maintained by the taxpayer. If your parent is a widow or widower, the claim may be made for you as a housekeeper as this will produce the larger allowance of £100.

Dependent relative allowance

A claimant may obtain £100 allowance if she can prove that she maintains at her own expense a person who is:

a relative of her own (or her husband's);
incapacitated by old age or infirmity;
not receiving an income from certain benefits.

A woman other than a married woman living with her husband may claim £145.

If more than one person contributes to the relative's maintenance, the allowance is apportioned on the basis of the contribution by each person.

If you are self employed

Tax will have to be paid on your earnings. You must send to the tax inspector, with the return of income form each year, a statement of business receipts and expenses. Keep an account of every item received and paid out in connection with your work. If you are using a room in your house as an office, a reasonable part of rent, rates, lighting, and heating can be claimed as business expenses.

A blind person's allowance

This allowance is available if the taxpayer:
is a single person and at any time during the preceding year
ending 5 April was a registered blind person; or
is a married man whose wife is living with him, and at any
time during that year one of them was a registered blind
person.

The blind person's allowance cannot be claimed in addition to the son's or daughter's services allowance of £55.

Social Security pensions and benefits

On which tax is not assessable:
Attendance Allowance
Death Grant
Invalidity Benefit

Non-contributory Invalidity Pension
Sickness Benefit
Supplementary Benefit
Unemployment Benefit

On which tax is assessable:
Mobility Allowance
Retirement Pension
Widow's Pension

A guide to what your tax-free investments are

National Savings Certificates
Index Linked N.S.C.
S.A.Y.E.
Ordinary Accounts of National Savings to bring in £70 tax-free interest.

Rates of tax

Your income, after the deduction of allowances and other reliefs to which you are entitled, will be taxed at the following rates (remember tax is calculated over the whole of the year):

Lower Rate 25 per cent on first £ 750 of taxable income
Basic Rate 30 per cent on next £9250 —do—
Higher Rate 40 per cent on next £2000 —do—
45 per cent on next £3000 —do—
50 per cent on next £5000 —do—
60 per cent on the remainder
Note: these rates are all subject to periodic changes.

Insurance

Insurance is a valuable investment channel. There are various policies available. A single woman should take out insurances to protect her mortgage loan repayments. Ask your insurance broker which he recommends.

Before you decide on buying a life insurance policy get advice from an insurance broker on which policy best suits your needs.

Charitable funds

Don't overlook charitable funds as a source of financial help. Below are some rough guidelines if you are trying to locate charitable funding. If you receive a supplementary pension a charity may be able to supplement your income through a grant for a specific purpose, e.g. to buy extra coal. The Citizens' Advice Bureau in your area should be able to direct you to a charity which could help. Charities fall into three groups:

> Those that are referred to as having a general charitable purpose and that help persons from some particular group, e.g. those with a particular professional background;
> Religious group. These generally run charitable funds or new housing schemes for those of some particular religious denomination;
> Those which help the people who have local connections with the charity.

The *Annual Charities' Digest* breaks down charities into appropriate groupings. You can find a copy of the *Digest* in your library.

Emergency savings

Regardless of who you are or how well you think you have provided, there is always an emergency payment to be made—a leaking roof, some gadget to help you with nursing, a broken window.

It is wise therefore to try to keep at least £100 accessible. Don't panic however, if you don't have £100 floating. It is true that there is a buyer for everything. In desperation I have sold my old clothes and in desperation someone has bought them. If you look around the house you will find something to sell—old suitcases, an unused bed, something. But for those who aren't so optimistic about simple ways of raising money there are short-term savings such as through a building society share account where your money is readily accessible.

Travel concessions

Make use of travel concessions when they are available in your area. The Senior Citizen railcard is now available to all persons of State Retirement pension age (men 65 and over, women 60 and over).

Many local authorities also have cheaper or free fares for pensioners. Terms vary from area to area and some places don't offer concessions at all. To find out more about what is available in your area, ask at the local Council Office or the Citizens' Advice Bureau.

SEVEN

Heating and Home Maintenance

You could suddenly find yourself trying to cope with large heat and maintenance bills. The following section is intended to stimulate you into looking for ways of saving in these.

Adequate heating is essential to good health and comfortable living; however, the cost of fuel can be one of the most expensive items in your budget. Therefore, it is necessary for you to have some information about conservation of heat, government heating allowances and conditions under which they are available.

Condensing the laws of physics, heat is lost principally in any dwelling through the walls and ceilings. In an effort to minimize this loss, it is necessary to insulate them.

Did you know that in an ordinary uninsulated house (and that could well mean yours) approximately 75 per cent of the heat is lost; 25 per cent of the existing heat goes through the walls, 20 per cent through the roof, 10 per cent through gaps between windows and window sashes etc., and 10 per cent through the floor?

Proper insulation therefore, must lead to a considerable conservation of heat and be reflected in a very much reduced heating bill. It is in your interests to see that the house in which you live is as well insulated as possible.

One cheap, very effective method of improving the insulation of the house is to use domestic clingfilm over the inside of the windows.

Insulating windows with domestic clingfilm
Because kitchen clingfilm will adhere extremely well to a surface newly covered with a clean, dry gloss paint, it can be used to insulate windows. By stretching a sheet of the film over the window pane and attaching its edges to the sur-

rounding painted surface of the window frame, it is possible to seal between the window pane and the film a layer of still air. It is this air that insulates your window. The amount of insulation you obtain depends upon the distance between the surface of the glass window and the surface of the clingfilm. A value of about 2 cm ($\frac{3}{4}''$) is recommended. Shorter distances make it less effective, but it makes little difference to the insulation if larger distances are used.

WHAT YOU NEED

A roll of clingfilm usually 30 cm (approximately 12 in.) in width, although rolls of 45 cm (approximately 18 in.) wide material can be obtained.

A razor blade or very sharp knife.

Cleanliness--clean, grease-free hands, and clean, grease-free, painted surfaces. If the paint is very old, apply a very thin coat of gloss paint to the window frame and allow to dry for 24 hours.
Gentleness, Care and Patience.

Insulating may be carried out without any structural additions to the window frame provided that the gap between the film and the window is sufficient, and that the width of the film enables you to obtain a satisfactory continuous airtight seal around the window pane. The method is thus particularly appropriate for insulating multipane sash windows.

METHOD

Take the roll of clingfilm and gently unwind one or two inches of the film. Suspend the roll by inserting your two little fingers into the opposite ends of the tube. Grasp the corners of the unrolled film between your first fingers and thumbs and offer up the film to the surface of the window frame with the film unwinding from the far side of the roll. Press the film against the paint and use your thumbs to knead out any air bubbles caught between the film and the paint-work. You should find that gradually the film will start to adhere. Holding the roll steady with one hand, extend the grip of the film on the paintwork by gently stroking and kneading the film with the fingers of the other hand. When a good grip has been established with the paintwork across the entire width of the film, allow the roll to unfurl gently, and lay the film under slight tension over the window pane. To increase the grip of the film on the paintwork, again press the film with the fingers on to all the framework surrounding the window pane.

Carefully remove the roll by cutting the film against the framework, with a razor blade. At this stage, the window will be sealed, but the film will be crinkled.

To remove crinkles, start at, say, the top left-hand corner. Pick off the film and break the seal over a short distance, stretch the film slightly and seal it back on to the paintwork. Repeat this process all the way round the edge of the film and you will gradually remove all the crinkles and be left with a clear, transparent, insulated window.

LIMITATIONS

The size of window that can be insulated by this method is dictated by the width of the film you can buy. For large windows one has to make a simple painted wooden frame to support the film.

Provided that it is not tampered with, the film will certainly last a year. Thus it is not a permanent solution to the problem of insulating windows. The film may have to be renewed for each winter season: but the cost of the film for this is incredibly small.

Fuel and warmth

Failing being able to use gas, coal is cheap, particularly if used in a closed stove—and it is economic in the long run to choose a more expensive type of stove.

Storage heating is less costly than direct electric fires, particularly if provided on the night tariff. Information on tariffs may be obtained from the local electricity board.

If you have electric central heating you can influence your bill only by your manipulation of the thermostat. The fuel board will advise you as to the most efficient settings.

If your mother's house has an open fire, and she is thinking about replacing it, ask the Environmental Health Department whether the area is to become a smokeless zone; if it is, you will receive a grant for the conversion and she should therefore delay having it put in.

Hot water is expensive. It can be made less so by using it sparingly, such as by making sure that the taps do not drip, and by providing at least three inches of lagging around the storage tank. Remember that the cold water that flows out when you turn the tap first on, costs as much as the hot water which you actually use. Try to draw hot water for a number of purposes at about the same time, rather than at long intervals.

A temperature of about 72 °F is comfortable; however, different people feel comfortable in different settings.

If your mother is a Supplementary Pensioner, she can obtain certain financial benefits in connection with heating. Thus, if she has restricted mobility, or any condition which necessitates extra heating (e.g. arthritis, bronchitis, heart disease, and other conditions), or if the house is difficult to heat adequately because of its size or layout, or its need of general maintenance, such as gaps between window frames and sashes, then the level of allowance granted is low. But if she is essentially housebound or is seriously ill, or if her house is exceptionally hard to heat, she will get a middle level of allowance.

If you are going out to work and your mother turns the heat up unreasonably as soon as you have left the house, you can protect yourself from an exorbitant bill either by having a pre-set thermostat installed, or by getting a mechanic to fix the setting on your present thermostat.

If you use an electric blanket on your mother's or on your own bed, note that the blanket should be serviced at least every three years by the manufacturer. If you don't take this precaution, you could be risking a fire. Read *Help with Heating Costs*, D.H.S.S., leaflet OC2.

Did you know that anyone can obtain a grant towards the cost of insulating a loft together with water tanks and pipes, providing there is no insulation already? The normal grant is 66 per cent of the cost of materials and work, or £50, whichever is the less. Applications can be made to the Home Improvement Grant Section of your mother's District or Borough Council.

Having insulated the house, it is then necessary to insulate yourself by wearing more clothes. As the best insulator available to you is air, you and your mother should wear clothes which have built-in air pockets by their very design and material. An undershirt (preferably string) or vest is the best first-layer garment, then a tightly woven blouse or shirt which will effectively hold the air in against your body, and over that, a woollen jumper or jumpers. If your mother is still cold, add a shirt over the lot and this should retain her body temperature so that she feels comfortable. It is important to remember that many layers of light clothing rather than a few of thick are best. As far as keeping her legs warm is concerned, wear two layers of nylons, as they will more effectively keep in the heat and be more comfortable than one pair of woollen stockings. Mittens keep the hands warm and leave the fingers free so that one does not feel restricted or forced to fumble.

Home Maintenance

The object of this section is to give you guidance in dealing with some of the problems which frequently occur in home maintenance. For more detailed information on any specific problem a library should be consulted.

It is a myth that a woman can't cope with household repairs—she can if she will learn.

Before deciding that you will fix the new washer or paint the kitchen you must accept the fact that you will need some basic tools—a hammer, screwdriver, pliers, screws, nails, branded adhesives, Polyfilla, brushes, rollers, etc.

First let us look at the problem of frozen pipes which, if not dealt with, can lead to leaks. Prevention is the answer here—lagging all water services in the loft could protect you from a flood. If the pipes run along cold walls in unheated rooms lag these pipes, too. In particularly severe weather it is wise to leave a tap slowly running. How vulnerable your house pipes are to freezing up and bursting depends partly on the kind of piping in your house. Plastic piping doesn't burst, copper piping is fairly reliable, and lead piping, which is generally found in older houses, is the kind most liable to burst. So if your house has lead piping take extra care about lagging. If a pipe has frozen, turn off the appropriate stop-taps (you may have to ask the man next door to point out the stop-tap the first time). Turn on the outlet tap and start to apply heat backwards from that point until you get the water running. The least accident-prone method for unfreezing pipework is to apply hot cloths along the pipe.

If the pipe has burst get a plumber in unless you are quite sure you can cope. Have a plumber's telephone number handy, for a burst pipe can result in furnishings being ruined and carpets being saturated.

Outside, water pipes and cisterns are particularly liable to freeze in severe weather, and to guard against this you should see that the pipes are insulated.

If there is a drip from the overflow pipe of a WC or cold-water storage cistern, the cause is generally a defective ball float or valve washer. To renew a valve washer, turn off the water supply to the cistern. If there isn't a stop valve then you will need either partly or totally to drain the cistern. Remove the cistern cover and use a pair of pliers to remove the split pin securing the lever arm to the valves. Then remove the piston to which the washer is attached (on some fittings you will find an end cap has to be unscrewed first). On the most usual model, you will be best advised to lever it out with a screwdriver. Remove the old washer and clean up the valve components, making sure to grease them before you fit the new washer.

If one of the taps drips from the spout (and a dripping tap can be a constant source of annoyance and aggravation), then it is generally a result of the main washer having worn out. To replace the washer, you must first cut off the supply to the tap. Only then, should you take the tap to pieces. The most common tap is a 'capstan' having four spokes on its handle, which is secured by a grub screw and will lift upwards when the screw is removed. The valve shield should be removed by unscrewing. If these parts do not move easily, pour boiling water over the tap to expand the metal and break the grip of verdigris that may have built up. When you use a spanner to remove the valve shield, wrap the spanner's mouth in adhesive tape or lag to protect the chrome plating. Next, use a spanner to remove the valve assembly by turning the larger hexagonal part anti-clockwise. Once this is out you will see the washer and will be able to replace it with a new one.

Drains

I would suggest you get in a plumber; you could wrench your back by trying to save a plumber's bill. However, for a not too severely blocked sink or lavatory, you can use a rubber plunger which you can buy at any ironmonger. Stuff a cloth into the overflow to make it airtight, half fill the sink or basin with water, then pump the plunger up and down over the waste outlet. If the blockage is a little bit more than a plunger can cope with, pour caustic soda crystals (handle very carefully, you can burn yourself on them) down the drain or one of the patent drain cleaning products will usually do the job.

Keep the drains and gullies clear of silt, grease, dead leaves, and other stuff which accumulates. If you need to, put on a rubber glove, cover your mouth with a gauze mask or handkerchief before you scoop out the debris. A protective grating fixed in place will generally save you this unpleasant job.

Decorating

Doing your own decorating will save you money and should ensure you a satisfactory job done at your own pace. The main clue to a good finish is in the preparation. When decorating don't neglect to remove furniture from the room and to cover pieces you can't remove so as to protect them.

Washable distemper, emulsion and oil paints can be repainted provided they aren't chipped. If paint shows signs of coming off or flaking, you should scrape at the area to smooth it down. Use a scraper to do this. Hold it as parallel to the surface as you can get it so you don't gouge holes. Use a fine abrasive paper to feather down the places where the old paint has been removed, otherwise the edges will remain visible. You may need to use Polyfilla to get the surface evened up with the area around it. Add the filler to water as directed and then mix to a creamy consistency. Soak the crack or patch thoroughly with clean water before you apply the filler. Sandpaper any such patches over to smooth them before you first use primer. The final step is to apply the paint.

If you must paint over an embossed paper, wash it down first, but use water sparingly or you will end up with a damp wall.

Wash off any area to be painted with detergent and water, working on walls from the skirting upwards. If you possibly have the energy to remove wallpaper do so, as otherwise old paste will sooner or later show through.

Before you paint woodwork, wash it thoroughly, removing flaking paint and then rub it down with glasspaper. Fill gaps between walls and skirting with fillers. Where bare wood is exposed, apply a suitable primer. The man at the paint shop will help you on questions of primers, etc.

105

You will need a three-inch brush for large areas, or a paint roller can be successfully used for walls and ceilings. When painting the ceiling work across and towards the main source of light. Emulsion and distemper are applied by working the brush or roller in all directions.

If you paint a ceiling you will work faster from a plank than from a ladder, but don't climb on a plank if you are alone—it can be dangerous at any time, but you will be more likely to fall if you are painting the ceiling and reaching backwards.

Always buy the best brushes you can afford; it will pay in the long run. Picking stray hairs off a painted surface is tiresome—to say the least. Enamel paint can be cleaned from brushes with paraffin. Get rid of emulsion with water, cellulose with cellulose thinners; varnish can be removed with methylated spirits. Be careful not to get spirit on emulsion brushes or water on brushes used for oil-based paints—next time you come to use it, the paint won't go on properly, unless you clean the brush very thoroughly with detergent and let it dry out completely—which is time consuming.

Hanging wallpaper

If you decide to hang wallpaper, choose a textured paper on a first job. In calculating how much paper you will need, treat windows and doors as wall. Cut your first piece of paper to length (make sure you have measured correctly) allowing at least three inches for trimming at floor and ceiling levels. Then lay the first length out and use it as a guide for cutting further pieces. When possible, buy pre-pasted paper, which has only to be immersed in water for a couple of minutes before it is hung. Keep the water trough near where you are working. To hang the first length, carry the folded paper over your arm up the ladder, making sure it is the right way up. Place it along the perpendicular edge and allow an inch or two surplus to overlap at the ceiling. Slide the paper with your free hand and brush the top part into place, working downwards and always from the centre of the paper. Then let the rest drop. Brush in sections until you find that the rest of the paper falls into place. Smooth the palm of your hand over it to remove air bubbles. Using the back edge of the scissors, crease the surplus into the angle along the skirting board. Then peel the paper back and cut along the crease mark. Do the same thing at the ceiling level.

Do not let the light switch give you problems. For a circular switch, cut a star shape from the centre point, stroke the paper into position and cut off the pointed pieces that are left. If it is a square light switch place the brush down the paper until the switch is reached, then press the paper against the centre of the switch to mark the position. Using the scissors, pierce the paper on that mark and make two diagonal cuts slightly out from the switch plate. Dab the paper firmly around the plate with a brush, peel it back, cut along the crease marks and brush it back into position. Quite easy when you know how!

Laying carpets

If you buy a carpet, you will often have to pay extra to have it laid. Therefore, it is wiser to buy a carpet square if you can and varnish around the edge or put vinyl tiles around it. Many people buy a piece of carpet actually to fit the room; this is possible if you have a reasonably small room, and although it will be exhausting to lay it, you will save several pounds.

Nylon carpets are more easily cleaned, and this is important to remember.

Carpet with a foam underlay will obviate the need for a separate underlay.

Putting a carpet runner on stairs is not hard and any carpet salesman will usually be happy to tell you how to do it. To keep the carpet in place, use gripper strip fixings which are nailed to the tread and to the riser of each stair about $\frac{1}{2}$ in. from where they meet; the angled pins being set to point towards each other. Lay the carpet with the pile running downstairs and start at the bottom.

Windows

If your house windows suffer from condensation, and are spotted with fungus spores, or the paint is peeling off them, make sure the wall and window insulation are adequate.

Mending a fuse

Switch off the mains current. Then pull out and replace each fuse until you get to the one that has a jiggled bit of broken wire in the middle. Use the screwdriver to loosen the two screws, one at each end of the fuse, and remove the damaged fuse wire. Put in a new wire of the same thickness and wind it around the screws so the wire is taut. Then tighten the screws and replace the fuse. Don't use the wrong size wire. If it is a cartridge fuse in the plug just replace the burnt out fuse with one of the same colour.

Fitting a plug

Take the plug to pieces so that you end up with a top and a bottom. Put the outer case of the flex into the cord grip hole at the base of the plug top. Lay the three wires in the plug bottom in their right terminals: from above—neutral (blue) on the left; earth (green and yellow) at top centre; and live (brown) at the right. Peel off the outer plastic casing of $1\frac{1}{2}$ inches of flex. With a sharp knife cut back the casing for about an inch. Twist the wires round their terminals making sure that the wires lie flat in the plug base. Replace the top and the screws.

Don't hesitate to try your hand; you may find you enjoy home maintenance and you will save a lot of money. But do call in an expert for a big or difficult job.

EIGHT

Sheltered Housing, Nursing and Residential Care

When you can't care for your mother for any reason, sheltered housing, a nursing home or residential care may be viable alternatives.

Sheltered housing

The advantage of sheltered housing to an old person is that she will be able to retain her independence for longer, and the advantage to you, the carer, is that you will be able to stay at work for longer.

Sheltered housing consists of any group of more than six dwellings with a warden service. The emphasis is on the preservation of privacy; everyone has her own living, sleeping and cooking units, and in most cases, her own bathroom. There is generally a common room.

Where needed, a home help and meals on wheels can be arranged for a sheltered housing tenant.

The presence of a warden ensures that the old person has a sense of security and support that she generally could not have had if she had stayed on in her own home.

Local authorities and housing associations provide this type of housing.

When an application is being made for sheltered housing, information on one's present housing, state of health and need should be given.

It should be borne in mind that not all persons adjust to sheltered housing.

For information on sheltered housing, one should contact the local authority Housing Department or the nearest Housing Advice Centre.

109

Nursing homes

A nursing home must be under the charge of a person who is either a registered medical practitioner, or a suitably qualified nurse, resident in the home, and there must be a proper proportion of qualified nurses.

A nursing home must be registered with, and be regulated by, the Area Health Authority and Health Board. Usually supervision is carried out jointly by a nurse and a doctor—the Community Physician for Social Services and the Area Nursing Officer for Local Authority Liaison. Generally these officials pay at least one statutory visit a year, and periodically drop in informally.

If your mother is suffering from a psychiatric condition which causes her to behave aggressively, it may be almost impossible to find a nursing home that will take her.

Most of the homes are comfortably furnished, have central heating and are well kept externally and internally. Few of even the better homes have sitting rooms and dining rooms. If your mother is still able to get about, it is important to find a home which has communal rooms.

When you go to look a home over, try to assess whether the other patients appear well cared for and, particularly, whether they are happy. It is often pointless asking them how they feel about the place, because they naturally feel that the matron may react unfavourably if they say anything critical.

Fees don't give much indication of the standard in the home.

There are some homes that are quite below par; staff can be impatient and even lack interest. Try to avoid letting your old mother go into one of these places. Most elderly persons find it very difficult to adjust to living in a nursing home, and some can take a very long time to settle down. This is very natural and can be blamed on the institutionalized atmosphere, stories that have circulated for years about such homes, and the realization that they may never go home again. Try to be as encouraging as possible, and visit often. Remember how you felt on your first day at school!

'Check out' any nursing home you choose with the Counsel and Care for the Elderly.

The National Council for the Single Woman and Her Dependants has a list of short-stay nursing homes.

Old people's homes

Old people's homes are establishments which concentrate on the provision of accommodation for the aged. They do not have to be in the charge of a qualified nurse and neither do there have to be qualified nurses on the staff. However, there are a large number of places in the charge of a qualified nurse.

Most homes take people who have to have help with washing and dressing, those who need to use a walking cane to get around, and those on a simple diet. If a relative is in a wheelchair, is incontinent or confused, it is therefore going to be more difficult to find her a place.

An old people's home should be chosen with the utmost care. The social worker can be very helpful in helping a relative to locate the right home for her infirm dependant. The amenities of an old people's home are important to the overall happiness or quality of life an aged person can expect; central heating, easily accessible bathroom, a garden, and other similar factors are important.

Settling in to a new environment can be traumatic; however, once they have settled, the majority of aged persons who maintain close links with their family are quite contented. A home with a flexible getting up and retiring time presents a rather more relaxed atmosphere.

There are three types of old people's homes—local authority, voluntary, and privately run homes.

LOCAL AUTHORITY HOMES

Local authorities in England and Wales are empowered to provide accommodation for 'persons who, by reason of age, infirmity or any other circumstances, are in need of care and attention which is not otherwise available to them'. Such accommodation is known as Part III accommodation.

Application and Procedure for Admission
You or your parent should approach the local authority Social Services Department in the area in which your parent normally lives. A social worker will visit her to discuss her need and to determine whether or not there is any urgency about the need for admission. An application form will have to be filled out with details ranging from how well she is able to cope to questions of finance. The financial information is needed so the local authority can assess what charge they can make.

Waiting time can vary from a minimum of about six months. When a place has been offered, it is expected to be taken up promptly.

Charges
A standard charge is fixed by every local authority for its residential accommodation, which is based on the home's running expenses. The maximum charge varies from one authority to another. The sum the resident is asked to contribute is assessed on the basis of her resources.

The amount of money every resident is enabled to keep out of her retirement pension is fixed by the Government. If an elderly person doesn't have enough means to meet the minimum charge plus the regulated spending sum, she may claim a supplementary pension.

The local authority may put a charge on the old person's home to meet a differential in cost. When the home is sold at the death of the old person, the money owing has to be paid to the local authority out of the proceeds of the sale.

VOLUNTARY ORGANIZED HOMES
Application and Procedure for Admission
These should be made directly to the home. These homes are mostly small, with less than 40 residents. Many are run by religious bodies.

Charges

These are set by each organization. Most homes ask for details of financial circumstances. The average charge is £40 a week. If an old person can't meet the home's charges, they can apply to their local authority to be considered for subsidy.

Information about Homes

Citizens' Advice Bureaux, Housing Authorities, and Old People's Welfare organizations have information services on these homes.

The *Annual Charities Digest*, found in public libraries, is a comprehensive reference book on voluntary organizations.

A booklet, called *Homes for Old People*, is issued by the Church Information Bookshop, Great Smith Street, London SW1, and gives details of homes where older members of the Church of England can go. The *Catholic Directory* lists homes for Catholics.

The Salvation Army runs about 40 eventide homes for persons of all denominations. Write for information to The Salvation Army, 280 Mare Street, London E8 1HE (information for women) and 110–112 Middlesex Street, London E1 7HZ (for a list of homes for men).

PRIVATELY RUN HOMES

Applications and Procedure for Admission

These should be made directly to the home. Your parent's financial circumstances and physical condition primarily will govern whether or not she can go to a privately run home.

Charges

The charges in privately run old people's homes cover a wide range—up to and over £80 a week. It is very necessary to check on charges and just what they cover before admittance is finally arranged.

Local authorities can assist towards the cost of an elderly person's living in a privately run home. If assistance is needed, an application should be made through the Social

Services Department before admission. Some charitable bodies will pay fees.

For Information about Privately-Run Homes
Applications should be made to GRACE, Leigh Corner, Leigh Hill Road, Cobham, Surrey KT11 2HW. GRACE staff have visited recommended accommodation. The information is free. When writing, the details of what you are looking for, for your dependant should be spelled out.

As privately run old people's homes must register with the local authority in the area in which they are located, a list can be obtained from that body. It is the local authority's statutory duty to inspect all registered homes to ensure regularity in standards.

Additionally, any old people's welfare organization or a Council of Social Service or Citizens' Advice Bureau should have lists of homes. The Counsel and Care for the Elderly also keep a list of homes.

CHARGING PROCEDURES

In the event of your mother's being admitted to a local authority residential accommodation, you should be aware of the 'Charging Procedures' and the 'Assessment Procedures', as they are called, because you may find that a charge has been put on your parent's home which you believed you would inherit.

The requirement to charge for accommodation provided under Part III of the National Assistance Act 1948 is laid down in Section 22 of that Act.

People provided with accommodation are required to pay for it in accordance with their resources within the limits of a standard charge, and subject to a minimum charge and an allowance for personal needs.

The standard charge is fixed by local authorities. It ought to represent as closely as possible the true monetary cost of providing the accommodation.

In assessing her ability to pay for her accommodation, the

114

local authority is required, under the provisions of Section 22(5) of the National Assistance Act, to give effect to Part III of Schedule 1 of the Supplementary Benefit Act 1976.

Up to £1200 of capital resources, however made up, together with any income produced, are to be ignored completely in assessing a resident's ability to pay. Each complete £50 of capital resources in excess of £1200 must be assumed to produce a weekly income of 25p which should be taken fully into account.

In assessing a resident's capital resources, any shares or marketable securities owned will be valued at their current market selling price.

If national savings certificates form part of a resident's capital assets, their value can be worked out from tables which are periodically published by the National Savings Office.

Where the whole or part of an occupational pension has been paid as a lump sum, or where an employer has made an *ex-gratia* lump-sum payment for a former employee on a once-and-for-all basis, the amount received will normally be treated as capital.

Capital held by the Court of Protection, or by a receiver appointed by that Court, normally belongs to the resident, and its value will be taken into account.

As far as a dwelling house is concerned, it is for the local authority to decide, in the light of the circumstances of each case, whether a person provided with residential accommodation has effectively given up residence in a dwelling in which she retains an interest. Persons admitted on a permanent basis will normally be assumed to have given up residence in their former dwelling. The value of the home will be assessed by taking a professional estimate of the property's current selling price, less 10 per cent in recognition of expenses which would be incurred if the property were sold, and less any mortgage or loan secured against the property.

Local authorities have no power to compel a resident to sell his property to pay the assessed charge out of available resources. When a resident won't sell, it is reasonable for the authority to put a charge on the property that would enable them to recover the built-up balance of the charges, including any interest, at an agreed rate, when the property is finally sold (for instance, after her death).

In assessing the resident's ability to pay, local authorities must assume that she will need for her personal requirements such a sum per week as may be set out by the Secretary of State.

The allowance is intended to enable residents to have money to spend at will. They should not be expected to use it to replace clothing, shoes, etc.

NINE

Death of a Parent

Knowing what to do when your mother dies can be of immeasurable help. Dying is a morbid topic, but it happens and none of us is exempt from it.

At the time of the death

If your parent dies at home, it is necessary for you to call the doctor. The doctor has the responsibility of issuing a Certificate of Death. If your mother has said she wants to be cremated and you want to fulfil her wish, you will have to have a second doctor's signature on the certificate. Ask the doctor who responded to your call to arrange for a second doctor to sign the certificate.

When your mother has died in the hospital the doctor in charge will issue the Certificate of Death. Again where cremation is intended, another signature will have to be obtained.

Once you have the Death Certificate you can ring the undertaker.

Then ring the vicar. He will be a tower of strength to you and you can discuss the service with him. Your next job will be to have your mother's death registered at the office of the Registrar of Births, Marriages and Deaths.

The procedure there is for the details on the Death Certificate to be entered on the register which you will be required to sign with the registrar's pen. (The death must be registered within five days in England and Wales, and eight days in Scotland.)

After this has been done, you will receive a copy of the entry, along with the Certificate of Disposal and one free copy of the Certificate of Registration of Death. Ask for two extra copies as you may need them; a small charge will be made for them.

After you have got the Certificate of Disposal you can proceed with the cremation or burial arrangements. More forms will have to be filled in if your parent is to be cremated.

Funeral directors are necessary, but you should realize that any dealings with them are business dealings. Therefore, you should take care to be very businesslike in your approach. Ask for a written statement of the fee he quotes you. Funerals are expensive. Anything more than the 'respectable basics' will be costly. If you want your parent to be in the undertaker's chapel you should ask him to arrange this.

You can arrange with the undertaker for the funeral to start, as required, either from your home or from his premises. Alternatively, you can request him to take the body directly to the church cemetery or crematorium and for the mourners to meet there.

When a church service precedes a burial, the coffin is taken into the church by the bearers and placed in front of the altar. The mourners follow the coffin. Some Anglican and Roman Catholic churches allow the coffin to be taken into the church the previous evening, and it remains there before the altar until after the service. Where the service has been held at another place, or where no service has been held, the coffin is carried direct from the hearse to the grave.

At the grave, the bearers lower the coffin into the grave on webbing slings. Committal words are said, and then the mourners go back to their cars and leave.

In case of cremation, the service either takes place at the church with committal words at the crematorium chapel, or the whole service is held at the crematorium. As the committal words are being said, the coffin passes out of sight either by a curtain being drawn across it or by being moved mechanically through a door.

If the ashes are not left to be scattered or placed in a niche in a wall at the crematorium, you can ask the undertaker to collect them and send them to you. Relatives often have their loved one's ashes scattered over a rose garden and then have a special rose tree planted in her memory.

A headstone or other memorial in a churchyard or cemetery is subject to the restrictions imposed by the church or by the cemetery. It is usually up to the family to approach the church or the cemetery authorities to apply for permission to do anything to the grave.

Although denominational burial grounds generally insist that their own form of service be followed, funerals do take place without any form of religious ceremony. If a body is to be buried without such ceremony, forty-eight hours' notice is required to be given in writing to the vicar of the relevant parish. In practice, most vicars will give permission over the telephone. Where no particular church service has been requested yet one is expected, the Church of England service is the one that is normally used.

If you want to inform your mother's family and friends in general, put a notice in the local paper.

The funeral director usually has one particular florist close to the funeral parlour who deals with floral arrangements mourners wish to make.

You can ask your doctor for a strong sedative to take on the day of the funeral. For some, a strong drink will help to see them through the funeral service and burial.

Try not to be alone. Accept a friend's or relative's offer to stay with you. Some people find that getting together with friends for a while at home after the funeral helps with their immediate reactions to grief.

The fees to people officially involved (the vicar, sexton, gravedigger, chaplain and officials) at the cemetery or crematorium usually have to be paid in advance. The general procedure is for the undertaker to make the actual payments and to add the charges to the total account he will send you.

Paying for a funeral

This can cause a lot of worry. The following points should be helpful.

If your surviving parent dies, you may well be entitled to receive a death grant. This is a small amount of money paid when someone has passed away, so as to help towards payment of the funeral expenses. Most people do qualify for this allowance, as it is based on the national insurance contributions of the person who has died.

If your mother was 87 (92 if your father) before July 5 1975, you will not be able to claim any grant. If she was 77 (or 82 for a man) before July 5 1972 you will be able to claim the reduced grant of £15. The full grant of £30 is awarded if your mother was 77 (or 82 for a man) on or after July 5 1975.

It is true that the grant is usually paid to the spouse of the deceased. But if your mother was widowed at the time of her death, and you are responsible for the payment of the funeral, then you should, upon application, receive the grant. However, if your mother made a will or if Letters of Administration have been taken out, then the grant will usually be made payable to the executors.

In order to claim the Death Grant, go to your local D.H.S.S. office with the Certificate of Registration of Death and a fair estimate of the cost of the funeral. You will be asked to complete the back of the form (Death Certificate) you should have brought with you, and to fill in the application form for a Death Grant.

There are many questions on the Death Grant form and although you may not know all the answers at the time, do not delay in submitting the forms. Simply say that you do not know the particular answers and that you will give them the necessary information as soon as possible.

A Death Grant form must be handed in within six months

of the death of your parent, otherwise no grant will be made, except in cases where there are extenuating circumstances.

Other sources of money to pay for a funeral can be:

SUPPLEMENTARY BENEFIT

This is a cash benefit towards essential funeral expenses that may be given if you (of course I am presuming that you are responsible for the funeral) get Supplementary Benefit or if you are working full time and your income is just above Supplementary Benefit level. Remember that you must go to the Social Security Office, before you can make the funeral arrangements.

A CASH SUM OR PENSION   may be paid by your parent's employer, her union, professional body or other; still further it may be possible to call on the deceased's insurance policy, or *any savings in the Building Society* or Savings Bank. It is possible for them to hand over £150 on evidence of death.

THE LOCAL COUNCIL   has a duty to bury or cremate a dead person if no other arrangements can be made. If it pays for the funeral it will claim any death grant due, also it may claim on the deceased's estate. Do not make the error of arranging a funeral and then discovering you are unable to pay for it, as the local authority will refuse to assume the responsibility for payment. When they do provide for the burial or cremation, they and not you will receive the death grant.

Bereavement

Bereavement is quite unlike any other experience you will have had. Most of us at this time feel that part of our world has been cruelly and unfairly torn away from us. If your mother was in severe pain or discomfort, you may simultaneously feel a sense of relief that her suffering has ended.

121

Generally, the first reaction to death is numbness, great shock (despite the fact that one knows it had to happen sooner or later), and a profound sense of disbelief.

Caring for a parent will probably have produced a particular category of relationship in which your mother has become completely dependent on your role as carer. For those who have been isolated over a long period through caring responsibilities, the loss of what is apt to be their only important human contact can be devastating. So often one hears grief expressed in such terms as, 'I am shattered; my whole world revolved around mother. Now I am completely alone. It is all so difficult. At times I don't want to go on.'

Grief, particularly if experienced alone, can take various forms and can be very painful;

'I had looked after my father for six years before he died. He was incontinent for a year and I seemed to do nothing but wash. I didn't like the idea of using sheets provided by the Social Services Department. I am too tired. I seem to fall asleep as soon as I sit down. The doctor says it's a normal reaction when someone close to you dies, and suddenly your responsibility has ended.'

Another carer said;

'Since mother died I just go from room to room, touching things that belonged to her. I haven't got rid of her clothes, they smell like her. When I get really upset I cry against her dress. She died a year ago. There wasn't anyone to talk to. The vicar didn't come and the doctor was too busy. At times I wish I wouldn't wake up.'

You may not be able to sleep, or eat, because of images of your mother that come to you whenever you try to rest. Your personal appearance may suffer considerably. Some people retreat almost irretrievably into themselves at this time.

The next stage can occur, either shortly after the funeral, or weeks later. You may feel frightened, confused and even

122

fear that you are becoming what is called 'mentally un-balanced'. Making decisions can be difficult. During this period, you could experience a sense of guilt. Many bereaved persons blame themselves for the death of a loved one. They go through the misery of 'if only I had done so and so, she/he may not have died.' What they are subconsciously doing is hoping that self-condemnation may somehow bring back their loved one.

Depression is common at this time. If you suspect that you are depressed, consult a doctor, talk to a good friend or confide in your vicar. Just telling someone exactly how you feel can be reassuring.

At this time above all others, great comfort is derived from a strong spiritual belief. For other bereaved lonely persons, the pub is a centre of outlet—grief can be shared—dying is one of the inescapable conditions of living, and none of us is exempt from it. An understanding nod or 'Yes, I know my dear' over a drink can mean a lot.

The final stage will come when you can accept your physical loss as part of life's overall experience, and you can look to a new life for yourself. Being able to talk about the pleasant memories you have stored up will mean you are over the first barrier.

Particularly if you are in the fifties or sixties, the outside world can seem detached and seemingly cold—yet in time you will re-adapt, and you will rediscover your place in it. Try to be objective, remind yourself that you could live another thirty years. The future quality of your life will essentially be determined by the effort you make on your own behalf at this critical stage.

During bereavement certain business such as probate has to be set in motion, and fundamental decisions such as where to live and how to manage on a reduced income have to be taken.

Below I have briefly described the procedure involved in administering an estate.

Probate

A will generally names two executors whose duty it is to administer the estate of the deceased. It is their responsibility to gather the assets, pay the taxes and debts, and distribute the remainder of the property according to the terms of the will. Usually, the executors apply for a Grant of Probate. Probate is necessary because some assets can be handed over to the executors only on its production. It is obtained from the Probate Registry, or if the net value of the estate is below £2000, from the County Court. Proving a will, or obtaining Letters of Administration in cases of intestacy is not expensive, and it may not be necessary to use the services of a solicitor. The Probate Office staff are usually very helpful and will generally explain procedure. The deceased's property may not be sold or given away until Probate has been granted or Letters of Administration granted. If there is no will the nearest relative must apply to the Probate Office for Letters of Administration to get authority to pay bills and deal with the dead person's property. You can get form PR48 from the registrar to find out what the procedure is. (*See* the section on Capital Transfer Tax for an explanation of death duties.) The personal representative must inform the bank, who will stop payment on all cheques and banker's orders and inform the Post Office, who will temporarily freeze any savings there.

Winding up an estate can take over a year. When a will is contested, it will take longer to settle the estate. The main grounds for claiming that a will was not properly executed, are that it lacks the testator's knowledge and approval, that he was not of sound mind, or that it was obtained by fraud or undue influence.

Often the decisions you have to make at this time will have far-reaching effects on your whole future life-style. The two most critical decisions will be where you will live and the overall question of finance.

First I will deal with where you will live.

124

Housing

Let us suppose either that you have always lived at home, or that you have returned home to live. Within a reasonable time you can protect the roof over your head by implementing whichever of the following is appropriate.

1 If your mother lives in a council house, you should have urged her to ask the Housing Department to permit you to become joint tenants, so that at her death, your tenancy would be protected.

2 In any case, it would be wise to have your name put on several housing association lists in an effort to ensure that you will have a reasonably acceptable roof over your head, either in the event of being left homeless, or for your own declining years.

3 In the case of your mother's owning the house, you could have asked and tried to ensure (hard as it will probably be) from the outset of your caring that your mother left you at least a life tenancy in the house under the terms of her will.

The following case studies are examples of the consequences of inadequate housing protection:

'By my father's will, the family house, built in 1936, is to be divided between my brother and myself. My brother had never cared about my parents. I gave up a good job and my nice way of living to go home. When my father died my brother refused to agree to me buying out his share of the house. He insisted on selling so we'd get more money for it. It is very sad, because now we don't ever contact one another, and I am quite alone. I suppose I'll end up in residential care—another face staring out of the window.'

Another carer said:

'I am 68. I took care of my dad for 16 years. He was crippled with arthritis and blind for most of the time, finally he became incontinent. At times I didn't get a full night's sleep for weeks at a time. It was very distressing to learn that he'd left the house to be sold and the proceeds divided among the five of us children. The others all have their own homes and never had a good word to say for the old man. Now I'm the one in a bed-sitting room, with my savings gone and living on a pittance.'

Wills. If your parent is an owner-occupier, try to persuade her to ask her solicitor to use clauses like those below when he draws up her will. This should protect your interests and ensure that you are not left homeless after her death.

After the general introductory clauses:

3 I give all my real and personal property whatsoever and wheresoever not hereby or by any codicil hereto specifically disposed of (including any property over which I may have a general power or appointment or disposition by Will) unto my Trustees upon trust to sell call in and convert the same into money with power to postpone the sale calling in and conversion thereof so long as they shall in their absolute discretion think fit without being liable for loss (which said property or the money representing the same is hereinafter referred to as 'the Trust Fund').

4 My Trustees shall out of the Trust Fund pay my debts funeral and testamentary expenses and all capital transfer and other duties payable on or by reason of my death and shall hold the residue of the Trust Fund in trust for such of my children X of A Y of B and Z of C as shall survive me and if more than one in equal shares.

5 To show my appreciation of my daughter Y having given up her own private life to take care of me during my infirmity and notwithstanding the direction for sale given in Clause 4 above I direct that the house in which I shall be residing at the date of my death shall not be sold during such time as my daughter Y uses such house (or any house which may from time to time be purchased in lieu thereof

in pursuance of the power hereinafter contained) as her principal residence and that until the sale of the said house (or any house which may from time to time be purchased in lieu thereof in pursuance of the power hereinafter contained) my Trustees shall permit my said daughter Y to occupy the same rent free my said daughter Y paying the rates and other outgoings and keeping the house in good repair and insured against fire and other normal risks to the full value thereof in some office of repute in the names of my Trustees PROVIDED ALWAYS that if my said daughter Y shall request my Trustees to sell the said house my Trustees shall do so as soon as practicable thereafter and shall at the like request apply all or any part of the net proceeds of sale in or toward the purchase of another freehold or leasehold dwelling house or flat selected by my said daughter Y and any dwelling house or flat so purchased shall be held by my Trustees upon the trusts declared by this my Will in relation to my said house and the proceeds of sale thereof.

6 If any of my said children shall die in my lifetime leaving issue who shall attain the age of eighteen years such issue shall take substitution and if more than one in equal shares per stirpes the share of the Trust Fund which such deceased child of mine would have taken had he or she survived me but so that no such issue shall take whose parent is alive and capable of taking provided always that the provisions of this Clause shall not apply to the provisions of the previous Clause.

Signature of Testator.

Signature of the two Witnesses.

There are rules about the format of a will: it must be in writing (etc . . . form P.8.11), it must be signed by the person making the will (the testator) or by some person in her presence and under her direction, and the signature must be at the foot or end of the will. The signature must be made or

127

acknowledged by the testator in the presence of two or more witnesses present at the same time. The witnesses must then sign (attest the will, it is called legally) in the presence of the testator.

Despite the terms of the will or effect of the intestacy rules under the 1975 Act, some persons may apply to the Court for financial provision to be made. The persons who may apply include a husband or wife, a child (including an illegitimate or adopted child) or anyone who was being maintained by the deceased person. The Court may order reasonable financial provision for maintenance to be made, out of the net estate. Application to the Court must be made not later than six months after the Grant of Probate or Letters of Administration. However, the Court may permit the later application if it thinks fit.

The maintenance can take the form of either a lump sum or periodical payments.

Among matters which the Court will consider if an application is made to them are the needs of the beneficiaries, the deceased person's responsibility towards the applicant and the beneficiaries, the size of the estate, any particular disability of the applicant or the beneficiaries and finally, the conduct of you the applicant.

Where, under the terms of the will, you have neither been left the family home outright, nor a life tenancy in it, you will have to find alternative accommodation. At bereavement, it can be very distressing to have to uproot. Don't make any rash decisions. Your brothers and sisters or any other beneficiaries who are to share the proceeds of sale of the house with you may be happy for you to stay on either permanently or for long enough to enable you to buy their shares at an affordable sum. Alternatively, if the house is large and in bad repair, you may be better advised to take your share of the proceeds of sale and buy yourself a small bungalow or flat.

If your mother lives in a council house, your continued tenancy will be protected on your mother's death if you have had a joint tenancy with her (the survivor's tenancy is protected). Where you don't have a joint tenancy, you will almost certainly be required to accept smaller accommodation by the Council. If your parent is a tenant of a private owner and if the tenancy hasn't already been transferred twice previously, you will be entitled to assume the tenancy at her death.

If you have been left the family home, examine the wisdom of staying on in it. The advantages are that you will have a roof over your head, that you will be in a familiar neighbourhood, and that you won't have the upheaval of a move. The disadvantages could be that the house is in a poor state of repair, needs a lot of heat in the winter, is in an area where muggings are frequent, isn't close to employment for you, or is a long way from public transport. Long term you may be better advised to sell and to buy something that will better satisfy your needs.

It is often unwise to uproot yourself to go and live near a friend or a niece etc., as they move or pass on, and you could be left feeling very lonely and isolated in an unfamiliar area.

If you have a large house, and/or you are nervous at night, the answer may be to take in a young person who is just starting work, or a student, as a lodger. This arrangement can work well where you retain your landlady status and invite him or her occasionally to tea, etc. Many youngsters virtually adopt their elderly landladies and remain friends thereafter.

Finance

While your mother was alive, you may have had her retirement pension, interest on investments, and the Attendance Allowance payment coming into the house for her part; and in your own case (assuming you have not yet reached pensionable age), Invalid Care Allowance and some Supplementary Benefit, bringing your income to basic entitlement level.

On the death of your mother, you will have to register for work if you are to recover unemployment benefit. But you can receive this payment only if there has not been a break in your contributions record.

As there will only be one person's income (yours) after your mother dies, you will have to re-think your whole monetary situation. Probably you will have used up any 'nest egg' you have had, and not kept receipts of any furniture, purchases, etc. to prove that although they are in the parental home, they are in fact yours at law.

A budget will be of immeasurable help at this stage (see Chapter Six). If you feel panicky, consult the social worker about what percentage of your income you should spend on housing, heating, food, etc. Additionally, she will also be able to help you with advice as to what benefits, if any, you are entitled (such as heating allowances, etc.). Budgeting food-wise buy *Food For One* from Sainsburys which costs 25p and is full of sound advice on food buying.

The other question that will present itself at this stage is what you are to do with yourself in the future. If you are not of pensionable age, could you go back to your old job; could you begin training for a new career, or will you, if near pensionable age, be content to use up whatever nest-egg or legacy you have and stay at home?

Employment

Work can be challenging, all-involving and open up new interests. Having to go out to work five days a week is good for the morale. Once at work, you will make contact with other people, re-build your identity and perhaps make friends among your colleagues. Your financial anxieties will be alleviated, and you will be able to afford to make some constructive plans for your long-term future.

If you decide that perhaps you enjoy gaining, or you need, extra qualifications, your local technical college, or college of further education, may provide the courses you want. Check

130

out their syllabuses through the Careers Research and Advisory Centre (see Chapter Ten).

If you feel apprehensive about how to get re-involved, send for the Equal Opportunities Commission booklet called *Fresh Start*. The address of the EOC is Overseas House, Quay Street, Manchester M3 3HN.

Marriage at this time could appear as a solution to many problems; however, the old adage 'marry in haste, repent at leisure' is as pertinent as it ever was.

With careful planning and perseverance, and perhaps encouragement from friends and family, you should soon be able to re-establish a satisfactory life.

Legal help

After a death, the services of a lawyer may be needed to help straighten out your dependant's affairs. Legal advice doesn't have to cost money. There is a 'fixed-fee interview' which provides a half-hour interview with a solicitor for £5. Ask at the Citizens' Advice Bureau for a list of solicitors who give these interviews.

Entitlement to legal aid depends on the applicant's means (disposable capital and disposable income) and for court proceedings additionally when she has a reasonable case.

If you get supplementary benefit or if your income and savings are small, then you can get free or inexpensive legal advice and legal aid. A solicitor can advise you on your eligibility.

Legal advice is generally available through the CABs —from 'Honorary Legal Advisers' who can give advice and write letters, or from 'rota solicitors'—local solicitors who give advice at the Citizens' Advice Bureau. All interviews with lawyers in CABs are absolutely free of charge.

Legal Aid Centres are run by volunteer lawyers and are open for a short period each week. For those wanting advice, it is essential for them to note just when the volunteer lawyers are available.

131

There are many areas in which you may at some time need legal help, among them are:

preparing a will;
disputes with your landlord or security of your tenure;
disputes with people over inadequately supplied services;
accidents;
preparing a case for tribunal.

There is also an insurance scheme available, through which it is possible to take out a policy covering fees either for bringing or defending an action. The premium is £15 a year at present, and the company which arranges this insurance is

DAS Legal Expenses Co. Ltd.,
116 Finchley Road, London NW3 (*tel:* 01–435 8431)
  or
1268 London Road, London SW16 (*tel:* 01–679 1744)

TEN
Useful Addresses

It is very important to know where to look for help and advice. The following are useful addresses. (Note that many organizations supply helpful booklets on their particular area of expertise.)

AGE CONCERN

This organization knows about the problems of the aged —that is its business. An Age Concern Secretary will be able to give you advice about most problems that the elderly face. She will know where you can find Day Centres, lunch clubs, transport schemes and voluntary visiting schemes.

Look in your telephone directory or ask at a Citizens' Advice Bureau for the address of the Secretary in your area.

The main body addresses are:

Age Concern (England) (National Old People's Welfare Council)
Bernard Sunley House
60 Pitcairn Road
Mitcham, Surrey CR4 3LL
tel: 01–640 5431

Age Concern (Scotland)
Scottish Old People's Welfare Council
33 Castle Street
Edinburgh EH2 3DN
tel: 031–225 5000

Age Concern (Wales)
1 Park Grove
Cardiff
tel: Cardiff (0222) 37182

Age Concern (Northern Ireland)
2 Annadale Avenue
Belfast BT7 3JR
tel: Belfast (0232) 640011

Recently I heard of one Age Concern enterprise in which a group of elderly lonely men began a club where they played bingo, cards, dominoes and had their pints of beer. Many older people, especially men, feel very hesitant about going to clubs for the elderly. Fair enough, no 'man's-man' wants to sit amid a group of twittering, chattering, elderly women, and no sedate old lady wants to be in a group of tobacco-chewing old men. If the option of a separated or mixed club is possible, all the better; that will enable the elderly to have a choice of milieu.

THE BRITISH DIABETIC ASSOCIATION

3–6 Alfred Place, London WC1E 7ED (*tel:* 01–636 7355). An information and advice service for diabetics, with the aim of keeping watch on the interests of diabetes sufferers.

THE BRITISH RED CROSS SOCIETY

This organization, generally known as the Red Cross, publishes excellent manuals on first aid and nursing, as well as arranging four $1\frac{1}{2}$-hour session courses entitled 'Nursing For The Family'. The course is designed to give the carer the basic knowledge required to look after the sick, handicapped, and frail. The cost of the course varies from county to county. As a back-up the Red Cross produces a card index (that looks like recipe cards) packaged in a box.

The head offices are at 9 Grosvenor Crescent, London SW1X 7EJ (*tel:* 01–235 5454).

BRITISH RHEUMATISM AND ARTHRITIS ASSOCIATION

1 Devonshire Place, London W1N 2BD (*tel:* 01–935 9905). Aims to meet the welfare and social needs of sufferers from arthritis and rheumatism. Has local branches throughout the

country and can advise on a variety of topics, amongst which are aids and equipment, holidays, transport, etc.

CANCER INFORMATION ASSOCIATION

Gloucester Green, Oxford OX1 2EQ (*tel:* Oxford (0865) 44654). Is able to provide leaflets on all aspects of cancer. Provides a telephone advice service.

CARERS RESEARCH AND ADVISORY CENTRE LTD

Bateman Street, Cambridge, CB2 1LZ (*tel:* Cambridge (0223) 69811). Gives individual advice on carers. Makes a small charge for this service.

THE CHEST HEART AND STROKE ASSOCIATION

Tavistock House (North), Tavistock Square, London WC1H 9JE.

THE CHURCH

There isn't anyone among us who at some time hasn't wondered about life after death. Some of us may believe we have some answers, and others of us may feel uncertain and anxious to talk about our faith with a clergyman. The elderly, mentally and spiritually, are often eager to prepare for dying. Their brothers, sisters, and neighbours die, and they begin to feel that their turn can't be far away. For many, making 'their peace with God' is very important. If your mother would like to talk to the minister of her faith, contact him and ask him to call. When he does call leave her with him to talk; your presence may inhibit her.

If she wants to go to church, but is too infirm to walk, and you don't have a car, ring the clergyman and ask whether a parishioner will take her in his or her car. If she is too ill to go and wants communion, ask the clergyman to come and give her communion at home.

The Church Women's Guild can be a source of relief sitters-in, or visitors. For a variety of reasons, you, like so many, may have neglected your contact with the Church for a long period, but you should never feel embarrassed about going back, as surely what is important is that you have gone back, not that you have been away. Faith can be a great sustainer, and many carers get through a heavy caring burden by having a deep faith.

CITIZENS' ADVICE BUREAUX

This nationwide organization can usually advise on the general subject of consumers' rights, tenants' rights etc. It can put you in touch with legal aid and with the more recently established Housing Aid Centres. Look in your telephone directory for the address of your local branch.

CONSUMER'S ASSOCIATION

14 Buckingham Street, London WC2N 6DS.

COUNSEL AND CARE FOR THE ELDERLY

10 Fleet Street, London EC4 (*tel:* 01–353 1892). They provide information and advice on accommodation and services for the elderly.

DISABLEMENT INCOME GROUP (DIG)

Toynbee Hall, 28 Commercial Street, London E1 (*tel:* 01–247 2128). DIG, an all-party political action group, pledged to promote the economic conditions of disabled people. They run a very efficient advisory service and besides offering a variety of information, specialize in help with financial problems. They have local branches all over the country, but not in Northern Ireland.

DISABLED LIVING FOUNDATION (DLF)

345 Kensington High Street, London W14 8HS (*tel:* 01–602 2491). The DLF is a charitable trust, whose terms of reference include all disabilities and the aged. It works on the aspects of ordinary life which present specific problems and

difficulties to disabled people of all ages. The Foundation runs a service which provides information on all types of personal equipment, aids, clothing, etc.

GUILD OF AID FOR GENTLEPEOPLE

10 St Christopher's Place, London W1M 6HY (*tel:* 01–935 0641). Grants made available to people who by reason of age or disability are in financial difficulties.

HELP THE AGED

An international organization set up for the relief of the distressed elderly, both in Britain and abroad. There is a monthly newspaper published in the U.K., called *Yours*. In addition, Help the Aged promotes day centres, hospitals and rehabilitation units. It is also active in the field of housing.

Help the Aged, 8–10 Denman Street, London W1A 2AP (*tel:* 01–437 2554).

THE HOUSING CORPORATION

Maple House, 149 Tottenham Court Road, London W1P 0BN (*tel:* 01–387 9466). Gives advice on a wide range of housing problems.

MARIE CURIE MEMORIAL FOUNDATION

124 Sloane Street, London SW1X 9RF (*tel:* 01–730 9157). This society can provide a night nurse for cancer sufferers. Ask your domiciliary nurse for details.

MIND (NATIONAL ASSOCIATION FOR MENTAL HEALTH)

22 Harley Street, London W1N 2HD (*tel:* 01–637 0741). MIND run an advisory service with social work support. They have legal and welfare rights officers who are able to assist with a variety of problems. Some of their local groups run Day Centres. For further information, the above address will put you in contact with your local association.

Amongst others, MIND have produced a very good book *Mental Illness in the Family* offering general advice to the relatives of the mentally ill. The cost is 35p, obtainable from MIND.

THE NATIONAL COUNCIL FOR THE SINGLE WOMAN AND HER DEPENDANTS

The National Council was founded in 1965 to help single women who have or have had the care of elderly or infirm dependants. It provides a service of information and guidance on financial and practical problems, holidays and relief services, and nursing homes offering short-stay facilities for the elderly and infirm. It campaigns for increased domiciliary services, studies legislation affecting this group of people, and promotes policies and changes to improve their circumstances. Has voluntary local self-help branches to support and guide members.

For further information, write or phone The National Council for the Single Woman and Her Dependants Ltd., 29 Chilworth Mews, London W2 3RG (*tel:* 01–262 1451).

NATIONAL CORPORATION FOR THE CARE OF OLD PEOPLE

Nuffield Lodge, Regents Park, London NW1 4RS (*tel:* 01–722 8871). This organization is a research body, with homes advice and information services for professionals involved in the problems and care of the elderly.

NATIONAL LIBRARY FOR THE BLIND

Cromwell Road, Stockport SK6 2SQ (*tel:* 061–494 0217). Private readers, public libraries and institutions may all borrow, free of charge, embossed type books.

NATIONAL SOCIETY FOR CANCER RELIEF

Michael Sobell House, 30 Dorset Square, London NW1 (*tel:* 01–408 8125). This organization provides financial help to pay fuel costs or buy extra bedding.

PARKINSON'S DISEASE SOCIETY

81 Queens Road, London SW19 (*tel:* 01–946 2500). Provides an information service for patients and their families to assist with the everyday problems of those suffering from the disease.

(See their booklets: *The Booklet for Patients and their Families* and *Parkinson's Disease—Day by Day.*)

ROYAL NATIONAL INSTITUTE FOR THE BLIND

226 Great Portland Street, London W1N 6AA (*tel:* 01–388 1266). For guidance on coping with blindness.

THE ROYAL NATIONAL INSTITUTE FOR THE DEAF

105 Bowyer Street, London WC1E 6AH (*tel:* 01–387 8033). For advice on how to cope with deafness.

ST JOHN AMBULANCE BRIGADE

Propagates the knowledge of first aid through pamphlets and classes. It works on a voluntary local basis, and local uniformed volunteers provide first-aid services where required. Many of the divisions run ambulances and provide services to assist the sick and handicapped.

For further information, contact St John Ambulance Brigade, 1 Grosvenor Crescent, London SW1X 7EF (*tel:* 01–235 5231).

SAMARITANS

This nationwide organization provides a telephone help service for those in distress or despair. The number of the nearest local branch can be obtained from the telephone directory.

SETON'S

These are distributors of Care-Call apparatus. Tubiton House, Medlock Street, Oldham, OL1 3HS, England (*tel:* 061–652 2222).

THE WOMEN'S ROYAL VOLUNTARY SERVICE

Check in your local telephone book. This service delivers meals-on-wheels, has some equipment for disabled persons, and sometimes supplies voluntary visitors and often runs lunch clubs. Their address is 17 Old Park Lane, London W1 (*tel:* 01–499 6040).

SCOTTISH ADDRESSES

Age Concern Scotland
33 Castle Street
Edinburgh EH2 3DN   (*tel:* 031–225 5000).

Blind Society for Welfare and Teaching
4 Coates Crescent
Edinburgh EH3 7AP   (*tel:* 031–225 6381)

Chest, Heart and Stroke Association
65 Castle Street
Edinburgh EH2 3LT   (*tel:* 031–225 6527)

Parkinson's Disease Society
10 Dunsmuir Crescent
Edinburgh EH12 7TD   (*tel:* 031–334 5716)

Marie Curie Night Service
21 Rutland Street
Edinburgh EH1 2AH   (*tel:* 031–229 8332)

Legal Aid
27 Drumshaugh Gardens
Edinburgh EH3 7YR   (*tel:* 031–226 7411)

British Association of the Hard of Hearing
38 Swan Spring Avenue
Edinburgh 10

SCOTTISH INFORMATION SERVICE FOR THE DISABLED

18 Claremont Crescent, Edinburgh (*tel:* 031–556 3882). An organization providing information services and advice, with

special facilities for professionals in the field, and a reference library.

WALES COUNCIL FOR THE DISABLED

Crescent Road, Caerphilly, Mid-Glamorgan, CF81 1XL (*tel:* Caerphilly (0222) 869224). The Welsh co-ordinating body for organizations catering for the disabled, be they statutory or voluntary. Comments upon all proposed legislation connected with the disabled and seeks to encourage the support of local and central government. There is a service of information on facilities and amenities for the disabled.

HELPFUL TELEPHONE NUMBERS
_____

GP
_____

DISTRICT NURSE
_____

HEALTH VISITOR
_____

SOCIAL SERVICES DEPT.
_____

CAB
_____

DENTIST
_____

EYE DOCTOR
_____

AMBULANCE (dial 999 in an emergency)
_____

THE NEIGHBOUR (by name)
_____

OTHERS
_____

APPENDIX A
Financial Benefits

Note that the figures quoted below (current at February 1980) will change from time to time. You should check them periodically with the Department of Health and Social Security.

Invalidity Benefit (Contributory)

After 28 weeks, Sickness Benefit is replaced by Invalidity Benefit, which is untaxed and payable weekly. It is made up of (a) Invalidity Pension and (b) Invalidity Allowance. These benefits are 'contributory', which is to say that they are payable only to those who have made sufficient National Insurance contributions.

INVALIDITY PENSION

This is a weekly untaxed payment at the same rate as the single person's Retirement Pension. (See Retirement Pension).

Eligibility

To obtain the Invalidity Pension you must:
  have received the Sickness Benefit for 28 weeks;
  still be unable to work. The authority requires as evidence of inability to work a doctor's statement covering every day involved; have made certain contributions to National Insurance (for details, you should enquire at the local Social Security office); not receive any other National Insurance benefit (see below).

INVALIDITY ALLOWANCE

Those who become unable to work more than five years before retirement may be eligible for this payment, in addition to the Invalidity Pension. This allowance provides some relief for dependants.

Eligibility

To qualify for the invalidity allowance you must:
  have been under 55 (60 for a man) on the first day you were unable to work;

not receive any other insurance benefit (see below);
have made certain National Insurance contributions (for details
you should inquire at the local Social Security office).

AMOUNT OF BENEFIT

Normally, the Invalidity Pension is equal to the standard Retirement Pension and an additional allowance for an adult dependant equal to a wife's pension on her husband's contributions. For details you should inquire at the local Social Security office.

FACTORS WHICH MAY AFFECT THESE AMOUNTS
Other National Insurance benefits:
Generally a person cannot receive the Invalidity Benefit as well as other benefits, but as exceptions to this rule she may receive, additionally, the Attendance Allowance, the Mobility Allowance and/or the Disablement Pension.

Sick Pay
Sick pay, salary or wages do not affect the amount of Invalidity Benefit.

Earnings
With the approval of the doctor you may work, provided your earnings are below a certain limit. For further details consult the local Social Security office.

Hospital
The total amount received is unchanged by a stay in hospital, if less than eight weeks' duration, by either the recipient or her dependant. For longer stays the benefit is usually reduced. For further details, consult the local Social Security office.

HOW TO CLAIM

If either you or your mother should become incapable of work get a National Insurance Doctor's Statement (from a doctor or hospital). Complete this form, not omitting the part at the back.

PAYMENT

Payment is made by the local Social Security office. The manner of payment is governed by the period covered in the National Insurance Doctor's Statement (see 'How to Claim'). If the statement covers a period of less than eight weeks payment is by Giro cheque, either weekly or fortnightly. In the case of statements for longer periods, you will receive a book containing orders cashable at a Post Office.

RETIREMENT
Upon retirement Invalidity Pension is superseded by Retirement Pension. This can lead to a loss of income, because Invalidity Pension is not taxable while Retirement Pension is. Generally, therefore, it is preferable to exercise the option of deferring retirement until 65 (70 for a man). This advantage is further reinforced by the fact that while in receipt of Invalidity Benefit you are credited with the National Insurance contributions you would have made in full employment. In some cases the additional period of five years will be sufficient to qualify for the full Retirement Pension.

RETIREMENT AND THE INVALIDITY ALLOWANCE
The Invalidity Allowance is unaltered by retirement.

FURTHER INFORMATION
The D.H.S.S. produces two leaflets: NI 16A and NI 196. Of these, NI 16A gives further information and contains an application form for dependants' allowance; NI 196 details the amounts of the latest benefits. The leaflet *Help for Handicapped People* is available from Social Security offices. This leaflet details a whole range of benefits and services for the disabled. (Although the Invalid Care Allowance carries Class 1 benefit it doesn't cancel Unemployment Benefit Regulations.)

Non-contributory Invalidity Benefit
The Non-Contributory Invalidity Pension (NCIP) is a weekly, untaxed and non-means-tested benefit, for those who have paid insufficient National Insurance contributions to qualify for the Contributory Benefit (see above).

Eligibility
To be eligible for NCIP you must
    be incapable of work and have been so for 28 weeks;
    be aged between 16 and 59 (64 for a man);

be a resident of the U.K. and have resided here for at least ten of the last 20 years and at least six of the last twelve months before payment starts.

You must not:

if a married woman, be living with your husband (or common law husband;

if you live apart from your husband, receive maintenance from him equal or greater than the married woman's Retirement Pension based on the husband's contributions.

(In either of these circumstances you should apply for the House-wives' Non-Contributory Invalidity Pension [see below].)

receive more than a certain amount from certain National Insur-ance benefits. Further information on these matters can be obtained from the local Social Security office.

AMOUNTS OF BENEFIT

This benefit is normally equal to the married women's Retirement Pension received on the basis of her husband's contributions.

SUPPLEMENTARY BENEFIT

If you or your mother are eligible for NCIP and have been or are about to be in receipt of Supplementary Benefit, you may apply for and obtain NCIP as of right. Normally this does not affect the total benefit received, but there are certain other advantages. First, the means test does not apply to NCIP, as it does to Supplementary Benefit. Second, you will, while in receipt of NCIP, be credited with National Insurance contributions.

To Claim

Obtain from and return to your local Social Security office a form which is attached to leaflet NI 210. The leaflet gives further infor-mation on this benefit.

Retirement Pension

Retirement Pension is taxable and amounts to a sum which depends on your age, the amount of National Insurance contribu-tions, and your present income from employment.

Eligibility

To obtain the Retirement Pension you must:

be 60 years of age (65 if a man);

have been accepted as retired for Pension purposes by the Department of Health and Social Security, with the intention of retiring on a specific date;

have paid sufficient National Insurance contributions.

The amounts receivable at full pension are, for:

A single person	£23.30
A wife on her husband's contribution	£14.00
A wife on her own contributions	£23.30

People who reach pension age after 5 April 1979 may qualify for an earnings-related Pension under the Government's new pension scheme.

These amounts are varied by certain factors:

earned income

age

less than full contributions to National Insurance

Earned Income   The effect of earned income on basic pension is to reduce your pension in the manner shown in the table below:

Weekly earned income (before tax)	*Pension is:*
Less than £52	Unchanged
From £52 to £56	Reduced by half the amount of income in excess of £52
More than £56	Is reduced by the full amount by which your earnings exceed £56

Age   At 65 (70 if a man) your pension is no longer reduced by your earnings as detailed above.

From April 1979 neither Additional (Earnings-Related) Pension nor Graduated Pension has been affected in this way by earnings.

Contributions to National Insurance   If you have paid National Insurance contributions continuously since 1948 you will be entitled to the full pension. If you have paid contributions intermittently, your pension may be at a reduced rate. This is a complicated matter, but your local Social Security office will assist you with any queries you may have.

The Earnings-Related Pension has been based on your earnings in employment since April 1979. If you were a member of a contracted-out, Occupational pension scheme, that scheme will be responsible for paying at least part of your additional pension.

GRADUATED PENSION

During the years 1961 and 1975 contributions could be made to a Graduated Pension. The pension so earned by such contribution is not large. The greatest amount anyone can get is about £3.65 per week; most men will in fact, be entitled to between £1 and £2, and most women from 50p to £1. See leaflet GR20A for further information.

POSTPONING RETIREMENT

A deferment of retirement beyond 60 (65 for men) results in an increase in the Retirement Pension. The amount of the increase is 1 per cent (1p in £1) for each eight-week period of deferment. The maximum deferment is five years.

LIVING ABROAD

Retirement pension is payable through orders which are valid for three months. Consequently, in the case of a trip of less than three months' duration, the orders will be cashable upon return.

For periods in excess of three months it will normally be necessary to see to it that payment be made abroad. This can be arranged by the local Social Security office, but be sure to inform the office well in advance.

The leaflet D.H.S.S. NI 38 gives important information about the applicability of increases in pension which may occur while you are away.

HOSPITAL

The amount of the Retirement Pension is normally unaffected by a stay in hospital of up to eight weeks. After this period, however, the pension of a person with dependants is reduced by £4.66 and for a person without dependants by £9.30.

After a year in hospital a person will normally have the pension reduced to £4.66 a week, but there are special rules applying to patients who have dependants. If you are in this situation, it is best to contact the local office of the Department of Health and Social Security, or the Welfare Department at the hospital, where someone will explain the rules. Leaflet NI 9 gives further details.

147

APPEALS

You may appeal against the amount of pension as worked out at the local Social Security office. However, you must do so by letter within 21 days of the date of the letter informing you of your entitlements.

If you consider that the reply to this appeal is unsatisfactory you have the right to be heard by a Local Tribunal and then, if necessary, by the National Insurance Commission.

The Attendance Allowance

This is an allowance which is non-contributory, non-means-tested and untaxed. It is available to those who are mentally or physically disabled, and who need and have needed close attention for at least the last six months.

Eligibility

Your mother must:

be resident in the U.K. and have been present there for six out of the last twelve months;

be disabled physically or mentally to such an extent that she requires by day frequent attention in relation to the normal bodily functions (at night the attention need only be repeated or prolonged) or continual supervision, so as to avoid substantial danger to herself or to others.

AMOUNTS OF ALLOWANCE

If attention is necessary only by day or only by night the attendance allowance is, in 1979, £12.40 per week. If attendance is necessary both by night and day, the allowance is £18.60.

These amounts are not affected by other benefits, nor by the recipient's personal income. The only thing which does affect them is a stay in hospital under the National Health Scheme. It is then payable, at most, for four weeks.

TO CLAIM

A completed Social Security form DS2 should be forwarded to the nearest local Social Security office. A covering letter should be attached to it if it is felt that the form does not permit an adequate description of her situation.

Following a medical examination by a physician at her home, the Attendance Allowance Board will inform your mother of its decision by mail. If you feel that your mother's condition really satisfies the requirements stated and if you are dissatisfied with the Board's decision, you should appeal for a review. Research has shown that the Attendance Allowance is often given on review.

REVIEWS

To obtain a review, you should write to the Board within three months of the date of their letter giving a decision. In this letter, you should emphasize any factors which you feel were insufficiently noted or overlooked before. You should then receive a copy of the report made by the physician, who carried out the physical examination. You should comment upon this report by post on anything with which you disagree.

Another medical examination of your mother will then follow in due course. Subsequently, you will be advised of the Board's decision (by letter) and the reasons for it. If the Board's decision is unfavourable, you must, unless there is a significant decline in your mother's condition, wait a year before applying again.

You can, however, apply for leave to appeal to the National Insurance Commissioner (another independent authority) against the Board's review decision, but only on a question of law (for instance, if you think they have not applied the medical conditions correctly in your mother's case).

PAYMENT

Payment is made by an Order Book and is usually combined with orders for any other State pensions.

Invalid care allowance (ICA)

This is a taxable but non-contributory and non-means-tested benefit payable to those who cannot work because they have to care for a severely disabled relative.

Eligibility
To be eligible you must
   be aged between 16 and 60 (65 for men);
   be a resident in the U.K.;

spend at least 35 hours a week caring for a relative who receives
either

the Attendance Allowance; or

the Constant Attendance Allowance, which is an allowance
paid with a War Pension, Industrial Injury or Disablement
Pension, or with workmen's compensation or equivalent
benefit.

You must not

earn more than about six-tenths net of the Invalid Care Allowance (ICA);

not receive the same amount as or more than the ICA from some
other basic benefit, i.e. Sickness or Invalidity or Unemployment
Benefit, under any circumstances;

be living with your husband or common law husband.

AMOUNT OF BENEFIT

The basic Invalid Care Allowance is £14.00 (about six-tenths of the
basic Retirement Pension).

SUPPLEMENTARY BENEFIT

To be receiving Supplementary Benefit does not make you inelig-
ible for ICA but the amount of the ICA would be deducted from
your Supplementary Benefit payment. However, ICA payments
have the very real advantage that you are then credited with
National Insurance contributions.

HOLIDAYS AND HOSPITAL

You may have a total of 12 weeks away from caring in any six
months' period without affecting your benefit. Of these weeks,
four may be used as holiday, provided you and your mother are not
then separated for more than eight weeks (in the same six months)
by stays in hospital.

TO CLAIM

You should obtain from a Social Security office leaflet NI 212 and
forward the attached form to

The Controller, Invalid Care Allowance Unit, Central Office,
Nonecross, Blackpool FY5 3TA.

RESPONSE TO CLAIM

You will receive a decision in writing. You may appeal against this decision. The process of appeal would be explained in the letter of decision.

The Mobility Allowance

The Mobility Allowance is given for the purpose of increasing the outdoor mobility of the disabled. At present, it is a non-means-tested, but taxable, payment of £12.00 per week. This sum may be spent as the recipient chooses.

Eligibility

To qualify you must:

be a resident and have been a resident of the U.K. for 12 of the last 18 months;

be unable or virtually unable to walk and be likely to remain so for at least a year;

be unable to go outside;

not have an invalid trike or a car supplied under the National Health Service, nor must you have a private car allowance under the pre-1976 vehicle scheme.

applications may be made by people up to 65 (men and women between 61 and 67 on or after 29 November 1974 may claim).

MEDICAL EXAMINATION

Unless you receive the Attendance Allowance, it is necessary to establish the requisite physical disability. This involves a medical examination. It may be expected that this examination will be held in your home.

TO CLAIM

Complete the form attached to the Social Security office leaflet NI 211 and send it to the address stated on that form.

APPEALS

1. If the application should be refused on medical grounds you may appeal to a medical board. The decision of this board may be further appealed against to a medical appeal tribunal.

151

2. If the grounds for the refusal are stated as non-medical, you may appeal to a local tribunal. You may appeal against the decision of this tribunal to a National Insurance Commissioner.

The existing Mobility Allowance may continue until the recipient reaches 75 years of age.

Widow's Benefit

These are benefits based on the contributions of a widow's late husband, made to the National Insurance Scheme. The moneys are payable to the widow and are taxable.

There are a number of individual benefits: (a) Widow's Allowance; (b) Widow's Pension.

Eligibility

To be eligible, a woman must be a widow and, unless she is over 60, must not now be married or live with a man as his wife.

(a) Widow's Pension This is a pension which is payable to a woman who was widowed after 40. The pension continues until retirement at 60. The amount she receives depends on her age, at the time of death of her husband, and on the contributions he made.

If he made full contributions, the Widow's Pension amounts are:

Age at husband's death	Weekly Benefit	Age at husband's death	Weekly benefit
40	£6.99	46	£16.78
41	£8.62	47	£18.41
42	£10.25	48	£20.04
43	£11.88	49	£21.67
44	£13.51	50 plus	£23.30
45	£15.15		

These amounts are reduced if the husband's contributions are less than full. Your local Social Security Office can supply details.

(b) Widow's Allowance This benefit provides a widow without children under 19 with an allowance of £32.60 a week for 26 weeks

152

after the death of her husband. Additional sums are payable if she does have a child or children under 19.

RETIREMENT

A widow can elect not to claim Retirement Pension at 60. If she does so elect, she can continue to draw her Widow's Pension and defer her retirement to any age up till 65.

Having retired, and claimed her Retirement Pension, her Widow's Pension, unaltered in amount, becomes part of her Retirement Pension. She then has the advantage of being able to claim her own, and half her husband's Graduated Pension. If, before she is 65, she continues to work after formal retirement age and earns more than £52.00 per week, she is apt to lose some of her pension (see Retirement Pension).

After the age of 65, the widow will receive the Retirement Pension even if she has not retired by then.

TO CLAIM

The registrar of Deaths will issue a certificate at the time of registration of death. The back of the certificate should be filled in and sent at once to the local Social Security office. A claims form will then be received. This should be completed and returned without delay.

APPEALS

See appeals in the section on Retirement Pension.

FURTHER INFORMATION

The local Social Security office leaflets NP 36, NP 32 and NP 35A give further information.

Supplementary Benefits

It is hoped that, shortly, Supplementary Benefit claimants will automatically be provided with a written explanation of how their benefit has been calculated.

Supplementary Benefits are payable to those whose incomes are considered to be inadequate to meet their requirements as laid down by Parliament. Payments are equal to the amount by which 'income' falls short of these requirements. These amounts differ with circumstances.

Eligibility

To be eligible you must:

be in the United Kingdom;

be 16 or over and have left school;

not be in full employment;

have registered for work, provided you are under pension age and are medically fit for work or have given up work to look after a relative who, in the view of your doctor, needs home care, but does not receive Attendance Allowance (a medical statement is necessary to support an application on these grounds);

have an income which the Government considers to be below the level of requirements;

be under pensionable age.

REQUIREMENTS

A person's requirements are made up of the appropriate supplementary benefit scale rate plus an addition for rent or equivalent outgoings. Discretionary additions may also be made to meet special expenses.

SCALE RATES (Weekly)

The scale rates for typical cases are set out in the table below.

Married Couple	*Ordinary Scale*	*Long-Term Scale*	
		Under 80	One or both over 80
Married Couple	£29.70	£37.65	
Single Householder	£18.30	£23.70	extra 25p
Other sighted adult	£14.45	£18.95	

(A) RENT

(1) Householders

Provided the sums involved are not unreasonably large, a householder:

(a) provided she effectively pays the entire rent, and provided that this rent does not include such items as heating and lighting, will have the full amount of rent and rates added to the basic amount;

(b) who owns and occupies the house, will have all necessary outgoings treated as rent. These include payments of mortgage *interest*, rates in full, etc. There is an additional allowance of 90p a week towards insurance and repairs. This sum is not altered by the number of occupants of the house. Sums payable towards the *principal* owing on the house are not treated as rent and so are not included.

(2) Non-Householders
(a) someone who lives in somebody else's household, but not as a wife, may add £1.70 in lieu of rent;
(b) someone who boards (in somebody else's household) may, within reason, have added on the long-term basis, the amount of board, together with £6.85 per week (£5.95 per week short-term, i.e. less than 2 years) for personal expenses.

(B) SPECIAL AMOUNTS
Special amounts can be added, when there are special needs. For example, there are situations in which special diet is necessary. Again, there may be a special need to have a telephone or to travel, or disability may impose heavy wear and tear on clothing, or some items of furniture. A few such cases are considered, but by no means all, and I must stress that a special need will *normally* be recognized and assisted.

(a) Special Diets   £2.50 per week is allowed for those who need a special diet, because they suffer from: diabetes, peptic (including stomach or duodenal) ulcers, throat or larynx ulcers, ulcerated colitis, and respiratory tuberculosis.

£1.05 per week is usually allowed for other medically necessary diets.

(b) Special Heating   Additional allowance is made in cases where more than usual expenditure is necessary for heating. For example, there is an allowance where the home is entirely centrally-heated, and in cases where the claimant or an elder person has difficulty in moving about, or where there is chronic illness, such as bronchitis. Again note is taken of cases where the accommodation is damp, or hard to keep warm. Further information is obtainable from Leaflet DC2 at your local Social Security office.

(c) Special Laundry Needs   Laundry needs are treated as special, and due allowance made for them when difficulties arising from

illness, disability, old age and incontinence are present, or where the home has no laundry facilities.

INCOME
Here, 'income' means the net amount received after deducting tax, National Insurance contributions, trade union subscriptions, fares to and from work, other expenses necessitated by working, and certain other allowances detailed below.

ALLOWANCES AGAINST INCOME
(a) *Part-time earnings*   The first £4.00 per week of any part-time earnings of those not required to register for work is not counted.

(b) *Wife's earnings*   The first £4.00 per week is not counted.

(c) *Part-time earnings of those who are unemployed*   The first £2.00 per week earned by someone, who is unemployed and required to register for work is not counted.

(d) *Occupational pension or weekly payment for redundancy*   The first £1.00 per week is not counted.

(e) *Disablement and War Widow's Pension*   The first £4.00 per week is not counted.

(f) *Attendance and Mobility Allowances*   These allowances are not counted at all.

(g) *Other Income*   £4.00 per week of most other income is not counted. Some exceptions are: child benefit, and most National Insurance benefits and maintenance payments (whether voluntary or compulsory). These sums are taken fully into account.

(f) *The effect of Capital on this calculation*   The capital value of an owner-occupied house is ignored, as is the first £1200 of other capital. But each £50 in excess of £1250 is considered to represent an income of 25p per week. This assessment represents an annual rate of interest of 26 per cent, so that it is clearly advantageous to use such sums for other purposes, perhaps the reduction of a mortgage.

EXCEPTIONAL NEEDS PAYMENTS

In addition to the weekly payments, equal, as stated earlier, to the difference between 'Income' and 'Adequate Income', the Supplementary Benefits Commission makes lump-sum payments for certain exceptional needs.

Eligibility
The need must be both exceptional and necessary to avoid hardship;
Not including the value of the house she owns and occupies, the claimant's savings must not exceed £300 unless they would be brought below £300 by the expenditure involved;
It should be noted that it is not necessary to be receiving Supplementary Benefit; it is possible to obtain these payments, while in receipt of an income which is somewhat above the threshold for Supplementary Benefit.

ARTICLES COVERED BY PAYMENTS

Things for which these payments are made include: bedding, footwear, furniture and other household equipment, fuel debts, hire-purchase debts, rent arrears, removal expenses and expenses incurred while travelling to seek work.

OTHER BENEFITS

Those who receive Supplementary Benefit, no matter how little, are entitled to a number of services free of charge. These are: dental treatment, legal advice, prescriptions, and spectacles.

Further information on these aspects are contained in the leaflet M11 which can be found at a Post Office or at your local Social Security office.

RENT REBATES AND SUPPLEMENTARY BENEFIT

In some circumstances, you are better off if you claim Rent and Rates Rebates than if you claim Supplementary Benefit. You should raise this matter at your local Social Security office.

APPEALS

Because many of the benefits are determined only to the extent that they are reasonable, it is extremely difficult to establish just what you should expect. For the same reason, you should appeal against an adverse decision on a claim or on a condition which has been attached to an award. Every claimant has the right of appeal to an independent tribunal.

The first step in appealing is to request, as of right, a Notice of Assessment at the local Social Security office. Unless you are satisfied with the information this contains, you should appeal in writing, to the manager of the local Social Security office within 21 days.

FURTHER INFORMATION

This you can obtain from the Social Security office, forms SB1 and SB6. The *Penguin Guide to Supplementary Benefits* by Tony Lynes is recommended reading.

If your mother is a hospital patient

The requirements of a person in hospital are to be assessed at such an amount, if any, as may be appropriate, having regard to all the circumstances.

If your mother is admitted to hospital for a short time, payment of Supplementary Benefit will be kept up at the same rate.

After eight weeks, if your mother is still in hospital, her requirements will be reduced; however, special regard will then be given to fares for visiting.

If she remains in hospital for more than two years, then she will be treated as a single person without dependants.

If she is in hospital, then £4.66 will be paid for personal expenses, plus an allowance for any outside commitments (rent, rates, and a standing charge for electricity). Hire Purchase instalments may also be included.

If your mother has a home of her own, then for the first three months, normal outgoings will be met, after which time the whole situation must be re-examined.

Arrangements for patients in hospital for the mentally ill and mentally sub-normal are similar to those set out for other hospital patients, except that the Area Health Authority has responsibility for providing them with pocket money.

Where a hospital patient is sent home or goes to stay with a relative, or friend, for a short period, she is entitled to Supplemen-

158

tary Benefit at the full rate for each complete day spent away from the hospital.

If your mother is in an old people's home

If your mother has gone into a private or voluntary home, and the local authority won't accept financial responsibility for her maintenance, the commission will take the weekly requirements to be board-and-lodging charge (or as much of it as is reasonable) plus an allowance of (in 1980) £4.65 for personal expenses.

It is essential to know the financial arrangements that will be likely to apply before she moves into a voluntary or private home. Some people let the patient go in before they find out about the financial aspect.

Housing related benefits

If your mother's income disqualifies her for Supplementary Pension she has the alternative of claiming a Rent Rebate/Allowance and/or a Rate Rebate instead.

It is necessary to apply separately for a Rent Rebate/Allowance and Rate Rebate.

RENT REBATES AND ALLOWANCES AND RATE REBATES

Although a pensioner may not qualify for Supplementary Pension, she may still get help with rent and rates. The process is to apply for the Supplementary Pension first. The officer who comes will tell her whether or not she would be better off to claim a rebate.

Anyone who pays rates can apply for a Rate Rebate. Anyone who pays rent can apply for a Rent Rebate. (If your mother is a tenant of a private landlord this is called a Rent Allowance.) Where she pays both rates and rent, she can claim a Rent and Rates Rebate. The amount of the rebate will depend on her income, how much her rent and rates are and who lives with her in the house. If your mother rents a furnished house, or flat, she won't get a rebate for the part of the rent which pays for the furniture. No allowances are made for water rates and the sewage charge in the general rates. These should be subtracted before the rebate is worked out.

To claim either your mother should call at the local council offices and get an application form. The clerk there will help her fill it in. She should go to the Treasurer's Department for a Rate Rebate and to the Housing Department for a Rent Rebate or Allowance.

If she can't go in person, then she can write to the council offices asking for the forms to be sent.

If she is an owner-occupier or council tenant, her rates or rent will just be reduced.

If she is a private tenant, her allowance or rebate will be sent regularly, generally by Giro.

If your mother is disabled, the amount of her Rent Rebate or Allowance and/or Rate Rebate will be affected—the needs allowances will be higher and more income will be disregarded when the calculations are being made.

See the leaflets *There's Money Off Rent* (for use in England and Wales) and *Rent Rebate—Read All About It* (for use in Scotland). For more information on Rent Rebates or Allowances, read *How to Pay Less Rates* (for use in England and Wales) and *Rate Rebates—Latest* (for use in Scotland), for more information on Rate Rebates.

These leaflets are issued free by the Department of the Environment (England and Wales) and the Scottish Development Department (Scotland) and can be obtained from your local Rates office.

Your mother can appeal if she isn't happy with her rebate or if her application is refused. She has one month in which to do so.

Appeal to Ombudsman

The right exists of appeal to the Parliamentary Commission of Administration, the Health Services Commissioner or the Commission for Local Administration, if you consider that there has been some maladministration.

To make an appeal to the Parliamentary Commission of Administration, you must make a written complaint and send it to your own MP. You should send any relevant documents, and it must reach him within twelve months of your grievance's occurring.

Among the departments against which the Ombudsman will

160

investigate complaints are the Department of Health and Social Security, the Department of Employment, and the Inland Revenue.

To appeal to a Health Service Commissioner, you should apply through your local practitioner committee within a year of your alleged complaint. Again, you should send any relevant documents. The categories of case with which he deals include delays and admissions to hospitals, inadequate facilities and ignored complaints.

When you want to lodge an appeal to one of the Commissions for Local Administration, you must write to your local councillor, who will pursue the matter on your behalf.

These Ombudsmen may have more 'bark than bite', and you may not get any direct benefit from your complaint. Nonetheless, the overall system may be improved as a result of your complaint.

The pension scheme operative from 6 April 1978

The pension scheme includes cover for someone looking after another person at home.

From 6 April 1978 it has been possible to get home responsibilities protection for the basic pension if you are unable to work regularly because you are looking after someone at home.

The pension protection for a particular tax year is available to those who have, for at least 35 hours a week for the whole tax year, cared for someone receiving Attendance or Constant Attendance Allowance throughout that tax year. It is also available to those who have received Supplementary Benefit so as to be able to care for an elderly or sick person at home. If, however, the old or sick person does not receive an Attendance Allowance, or you do not receive Supplementary Benefit then you *must* continue to pay the Class III contributions (voluntary) but, if you are within five years of pension age you may already have enough contributions for the standard rate of basic pension. The local Social Security office will advise you if you write to them quoting your appropriate National Insurance number.

When your basic pension is being worked out, the number of years for which you have received home responsibilities protection, will be taken away from the number of qualifying years of contributions you need for full pension. The full basic pension will be

161

amended if you have this reduced number of qualifying years, provided it is not less than 20.

Occupational pension scheme

There are three methods of determining an occupational pension.

(a) The final salary plan is probably the most satisfactory form of pension arrangement. This scheme works on the assumption that earnings are at their height in the year or years immediately before retirement. A formula is used providing a pensioner with a fraction of her final salary for each year of employment. One-sixtieth of the final salary for each year's service is common.

(b) The money-purchase scheme invests each member's contribution through an insurance company. She will therefore be provided with a pension on her behalf strictly in accordance with her contributions.

(c) The average pay scheme provides a pension related to year-by-year pay. For those whose pay rises rapidly, this is a good scheme.

PENSION ON RETIREMENT

The maximum allowed by the Inland Revenue is two-thirds of final salary.

162

APPENDIX B
Recommended Further Reading

Directory for the Disabled, ed. Ann Darnborough and Derek Kinrade. Woodhead and Faulkner 1977.

Incontinence, Dorothy Mandelstan. Heinemann Health Book For Disabled Living Foundation 1977.

Lady Watch your Money, Heather McKenzie. John Clare Books 1980.

Return to Mobility, Margaret Hawker. The Chest, Heart and Stroke Association 1978.

Supplementary Benefits handbook, produced for the Department of Health and Social Security by Her Majesty's Stationery Office February 1977.

Take Care of Your Elderly Relative, J. A. Muir Gray and Heather McKenzie. George Allen and Unwin and Beaconsfield Publishers 1980.

Take Care of Yourself, Donald Vickery, James Fries, J. A. Muir Gray, and Simon Smail, George Allen and Unwin 1979.

Your Rights, Age Concern 1980. Obtainable from Bernard Sunley House, 60 Pitcairn Road, Mitcham, Surrey. Price 55p.

The Getting-On Catalogue, Heather McKenzie and Ashley Bruce. John Clare Books 1980.

Index

Those organizations referred to in the text are included in the index, except
those on the alphabetical list on pages 133–41

165

166

167

168